CLIVE BARKER was bo
He is the author of *The Boo*
The Damnation Game, Weaveworld, Cabal, The Great and Secret Show, The Hellbound Heart, Imajica and *The Thief of Always.* In addition to his work as a novelist and short story writer, he is also an accomplished illustrator and writes, directs and produces for the stage and screen. His spectacular films the *Hellraiser* trilogy, *Nightbreed* and *Candyman* bring his unique and indelible vision of modern horror to celluloid and video life. Barker uses all aspects of popular culture to substantiate his extraordinary insight into the menacing present. Millions of readers and filmgoers have been captivated by Barker's prodigious talents; now graphic novel adaptations of his stories add a further dimension to his hold on the popular imagination. Clive Barker lives in Los Angeles, where he continues his love affair with the bizarre, the perverse and the terrifying.

INTERNATIONAL ACCLAIM FOR
CLIVE BARKER:

'Barker is so good I am almost tongue-tied. What Barker does makes the rest of us look like we've been asleep for the last ten years.'

STEPHEN KING

'A powerful and fascinating writer with a brilliant imagination.'

J.G.BALLARD

'Clive Barker has been an amazing writer from his first appearance, with great gifts of invention and commitment to his own vision stamped on every page.'

PETER STRAUB

BOOKS BY CLIVE BARKER

The Books of Blood (*six volumes*)
The Damnation Game
Weaveworld
Cabal
The Great and Secret Show
The Hellbound Heart
Imajica
The Thief of Always
Clive Barker, Illustrator

GRAPHIC STORIES BY CLIVE BARKER

Tapping the Vein (*five volumes*)
Son of Celluloid

THE ARTISTS

John Bolton

lives in North London, painting in his eerie, prop-filled studio. (Many of the extraordinary objects surrounding his drawing board are dead or asleep.) He studied illustration and design at East Ham Technical College, in East London, and worked for British magazines and book publishers, painting covers and artwork. He began working in comics in the late 1970s and eventually broke into the big American comic market, expanding his field to include work on a number of movies. He is currently working on *Man-Bat*, the latest Batman epic. He has produced the graphic adaptation of *Army of Darkness*, Sam Raimi's film, and contributed to the graphic novel adaptation of the album *Freak Show* by the Residents.

Hector Gomez

was born in Argentina and now lives in Brazil. He has had two graphic novels published in Brazil, *Samsara* and *Amazing Muchachas.* He works as an illustrator for mainstream magazines and exhibits canvases at exhibitions. His covers for Malibu Comics include *Dollman*, *Rocket Ranger*, *Jungle Love* and *Paranoia.*

CLIVE BARKER

THE YATTERING AND JACK

Adapted by Steve Niles
Illustrated by John Bolton

AND

HOW SPOILERS BLEED

Adapted by Steve Niles and Fred Burke
Illustrated by Hector Gomez

EclipseGraphicNovels
An Imprint of HarperCollins*Publishers*

Eclipse Graphic Novels
An Imprint of HarperCollins*Publishers*,
77–85 Fulham Palace Road,
Hammersmith, London W6 8JB

Published by Eclipse Graphic Novels 1993
9 8 7 6 5 4 3 2 1

ISBN 0 586 21750 9

Printed and bound in Hong Kong

WHY THE POWERS (LONG MAY THEY HOLD COURT; LONG MAY THEY SHIT LIGHT ON THE HEADS OF THE DAMNED) HAD SENT IT OUT FROM HELL, FROM HOME, THE YATTERING COULDN'T DISCOVER.

WHENEVER IT PASSED A TENTATIVE INQUIRY ALONG THE SYSTEM TO ITS MASTER, JUST ASKING THE SIMPLE QUESTION, "WHAT AM I DOING HERE?", IT WAS ANSWERED WITH A SWIFT REBUKE FOR ITS CURIOSITY.

NONE OF ITS BUSINESS! CAME THE REPLY, ITS BUSINESS WAS TO DO.

OR DIE TRYING.

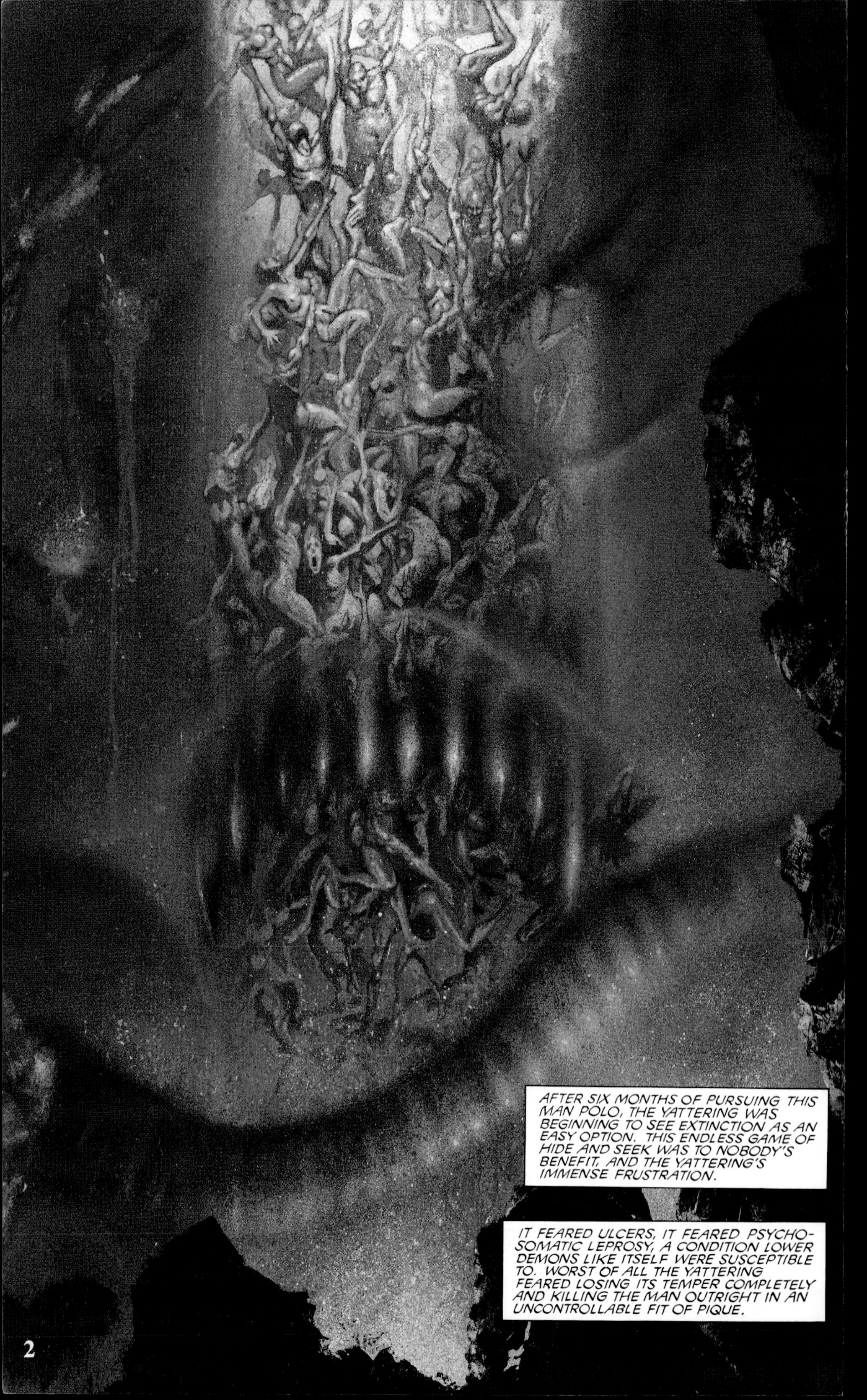
AFTER SIX MONTHS OF PURSUING THIS MAN POLO, THE YATTERING WAS BEGINNING TO SEE EXTINCTION AS AN EASY OPTION. THIS ENDLESS GAME OF HIDE AND SEEK WAS TO NOBODY'S BENEFIT, AND THE YATTERING'S IMMENSE FRUSTRATION.
IT FEARED ULCERS, IT FEARED PSYCHO-SOMATIC LEPROSY, A CONDITION LOWER DEMONS LIKE ITSELF WERE SUSCEPTIBLE TO. WORST OF ALL THE YATTERING FEARED LOSING ITS TEMPER COMPLETELY AND KILLING THE MAN OUTRIGHT IN AN UNCONTROLLABLE FIT OF PIQUE.

WHAT WAS JACK POLO ANYWAY?
A GHERKIN IMPORTER; BY THE BALLS OF LEVITICUS, THE MAN WAS SIMPLY A PICKLE IMPORTER. HIS LIFE WAS WORN OUT, HIS FAMILY WAS DULL, HIS POLITICS WERE SIMPLE-MINDED AND HIS THEOLOGY NONEXISTENT.
THE MAN WAS A NO-ACCOUNT, ONE OF NATURE'S BLANKEST LITTLE NUMBERS-- WHY BOTHER WITH THE LIKES OF HIM? THIS WASN'T A FAUST: A PACT-MAKER, A SOUL SELLER.
THIS ONE WOULDN'T LOOK TWICE AT THE CHANCE OF DIVINE INSPIRATION: HE'D SNIFF, SHRUG AND GET ON WITH HIS GHERKIN IMPORTING.

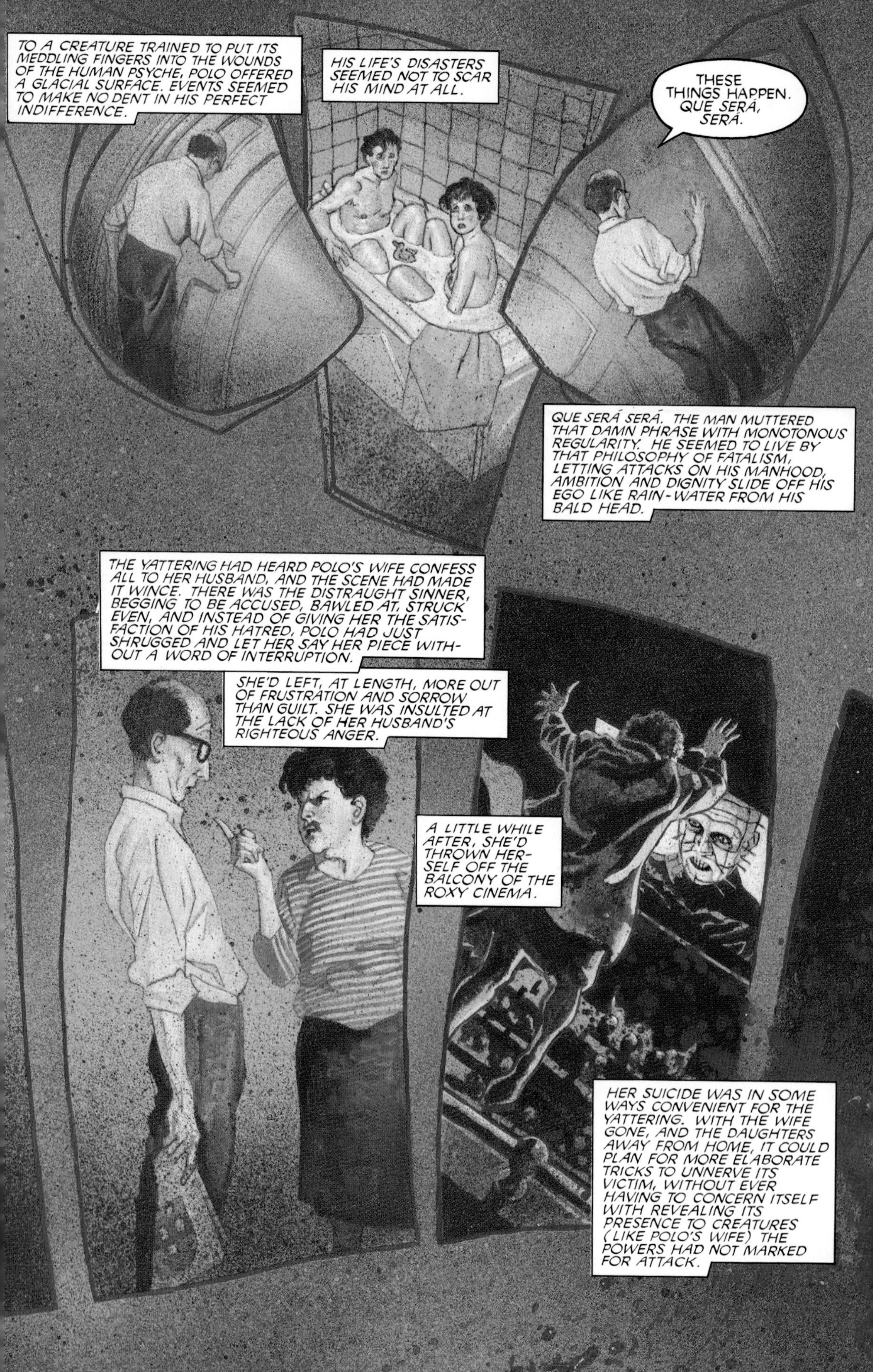
TO A CREATURE TRAINED TO PUT ITS MEDDLING FINGERS INTO THE WOUNDS OF THE HUMAN PSYCHE, POLO OFFERED A GLACIAL SURFACE. EVENTS SEEMED TO MAKE NO DENT IN HIS PERFECT INDIFFERENCE.
HIS LIFE'S DISASTERS SEEMED NOT TO SCAR HIS MIND AT ALL.
THESE THINGS HAPPEN. QUE SERÁ, SERÁ.
QUE SERÁ SERÁ. THE MAN MUTTERED THAT DAMN PHRASE WITH MONOTONOUS REGULARITY. HE SEEMED TO LIVE BY THAT PHILOSOPHY OF FATALISM, LETTING ATTACKS ON HIS MANHOOD, AMBITION AND DIGNITY SLIDE OFF HIS EGO LIKE RAIN-WATER FROM HIS BALD HEAD.
THE YATTERING HAD HEARD POLO'S WIFE CONFESS ALL TO HER HUSBAND, AND THE SCENE HAD MADE IT WINCE. THERE WAS THE DISTRAUGHT SINNER, BEGGING TO BE ACCUSED, BAWLED AT, STRUCK EVEN, AND INSTEAD OF GIVING HER THE SATIS-FACTION OF HIS HATRED, POLO HAD JUST SHRUGGED AND LET HER SAY HER PIECE WITH-OUT A WORD OF INTERRUPTION.
SHE'D LEFT, AT LENGTH, MORE OUT OF FRUSTRATION AND SORROW THAN GUILT. SHE WAS INSULTED AT THE LACK OF HER HUSBAND'S RIGHTEOUS ANGER.
A LITTLE WHILE AFTER, SHE'D THROWN HER-SELF OFF THE BALCONY OF THE ROXY CINEMA.
HER SUICIDE WAS IN SOME WAYS CONVENIENT FOR THE YATTERING. WITH THE WIFE GONE, AND THE DAUGHTERS AWAY FROM HOME, IT COULD PLAN FOR MORE ELABORATE TRICKS TO UNNERVE ITS VICTIM, WITHOUT EVER HAVING TO CONCERN ITSELF WITH REVEALING ITS PRESENCE TO CREATURES (LIKE POLO'S WIFE) THE POWERS HAD NOT MARKED FOR ATTACK.

YET THE YATTERING
WAS BOUND...

...BOUND TO THAT HOUSE, LONG NIGHT AND LONGER DAY, UNTIL HE HAD THE MAN A LUNATIC, OR AS GOOD AS.

IT WAS GOING TO BE A LENGTHY JOB, IF NOT INTERMINABLE.

YES, THERE WERE TIMES WHEN EVEN PSYCHOSOMATIC LEPROSY WOULD BE BEARABLE IF IT MEANT BEING FREE OF THIS IMPOSSIBLE MISSION.

FOR HIS PART, JACK POLO WAS THE MOST UNKNOWING OF MEN. HE HAD ALWAYS BEEN THAT WAY; INDEED HIS HISTORY WAS LITTERED WITH THE VICTIMS OF HIS NAIVETE.

WHEN HIS LATE, LAMENTED WIFE HAD CHEATED ON HIM HE WAS THE LAST TO FIND OUT. AND THE CLUES THEY'D LEFT BEHIND THEM! A BLIND, DEAF AND DUMB MAN WOULD HAVE BECOME SUSPICIOUS.

NOT JACK. HE POTTERED ABOUT HIS DULL BUSINESS AND NEVER NOTICED THE TANG OF THE ADULTERER'S COLOGNE, NOR THE ABNORMAL REGULARITY WITH WHICH HIS WIFE CHANGED THE BED LINEN.

HE WAS NO LESS UNINTERESTED IN EVENTS WHEN HIS YOUNGER DAUGHTER AMANDA CONFESSED HER LESBIANISM TO HIM.

WELL, AS LONG AS YOU DON'T GET PREGNANT, DARLING.

WHAT CHANCE DID A FURY HAVE WITH A MAN LIKE THAT?

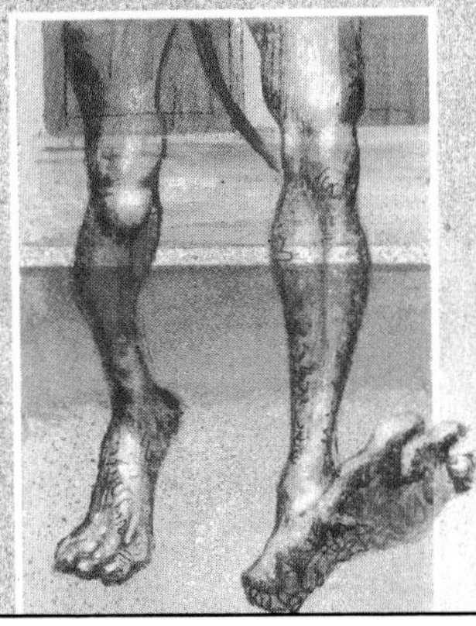

BUT THE ABSENCE OF THE WIFE LEFT THE HOUSE EMPTY DURING THE DAYS, AND THAT BECAME A BURDEN.

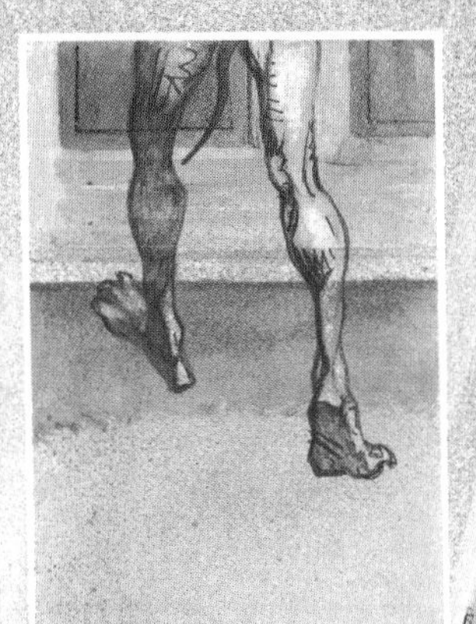

A BURDEN OF BOREDOM THE YATTERING FOUND SCARCELY SUPPORTABLE.

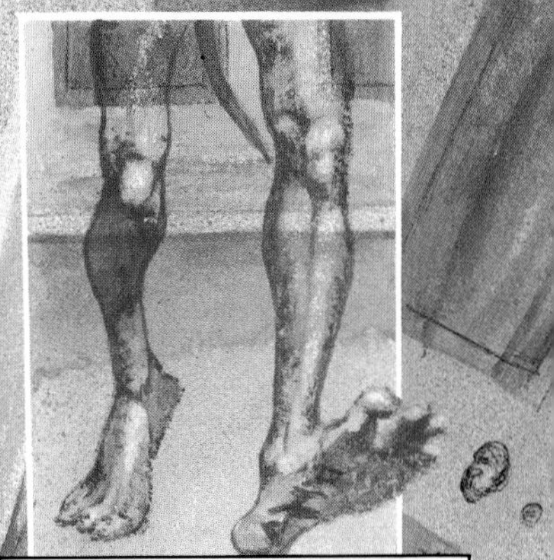

THE HOURS FROM NINE TO FIVE, ALONE IN THE HOUSE, OFTEN SEEMED ENDLESS.

IT WOULD MOPE AND WANDER, PLANNING BIZARRE AND IMPRACTICAL REVENGES UPON THE POLO-MAN, PACING THE ROOMS, HEARTSICK, COMPANIONED ONLY BY THE CLICKS AND WHIRRS OF THE HOUSE.

THE SITUATION RAPIDLY BECAME SO DESPERATE THAT THE MIDDAY MAIL DROP BECAME THE HIGH POINT OF THE DAY.

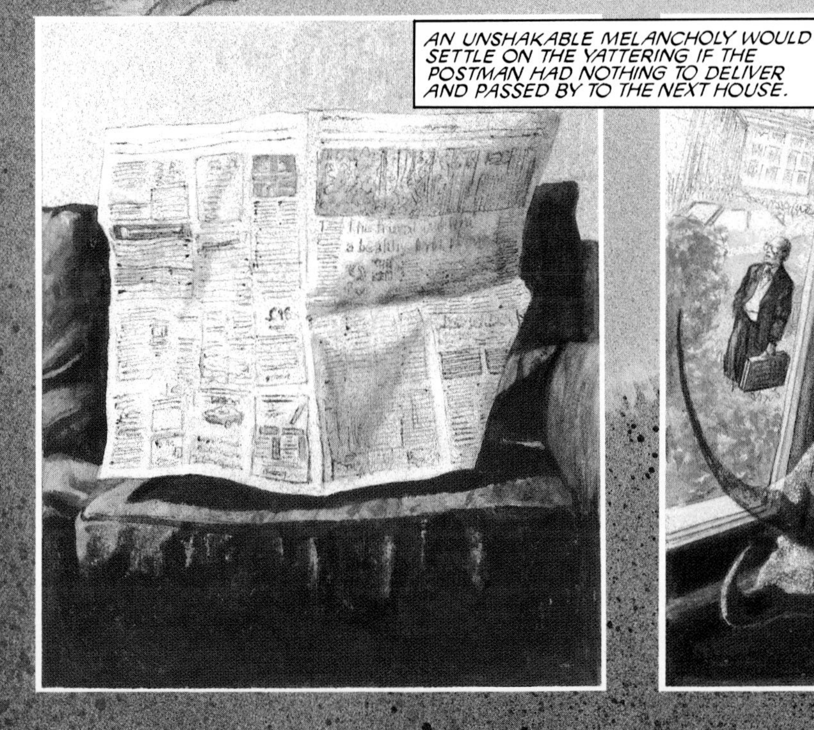

AN UNSHAKABLE MELANCHOLY WOULD SETTLE ON THE YATTERING IF THE POSTMAN HAD NOTHING TO DELIVER AND PASSED BY TO THE NEXT HOUSE.

WHEN JACK RETURNED, THE GAMES WOULD BEGIN IN EARNEST.

THE USUAL WARM-UP ROUTINE: IT WOULD MEET JACK AT THE DOOR AND PREVENT HIS KEY FROM TURNING IN THE LOCK.

THE CONTEST WOULD GO ON UNTIL JACK ACCIDENTALLY FOUND THE MEASURE OF THE YATTERING'S RESISTANCE, AND WON THE DAY.

SUBSIDENCE... QUE SERÁ SERÁ.

IN THE BATHROOM, THE YATTERING WOULD HAVE SQUEEZED TOOTHPASTE AROUND THE TOILET SEAT AND HAVE PLUGGED UP THE SHOWER HEAD WITH SOGGY TOILET PAPER.

IT WOULD EVEN SHARE THE SHOWER WITH JACK, UNSEEN, MURMURING OBSCENE SUGGESTIONS IN HIS EAR.

THAT WAS ALWAYS SUCCESSFUL, THE DEMONS WERE TAUGHT AT THE ACADEMY. THE OBSCENITIES IN THE EAR ROUTINE NEVER FAILED TO DISTRESS CLIENTS, MAKING THEM THINK THEY WERE CONCEIVING OF THESE PERNICIOUS ACTS THEMSELVES, AND DRIVING THEM TO SELF-DISGUST, THEN TO SELF-REJECTION, AND FINALLY TO MADNESS.

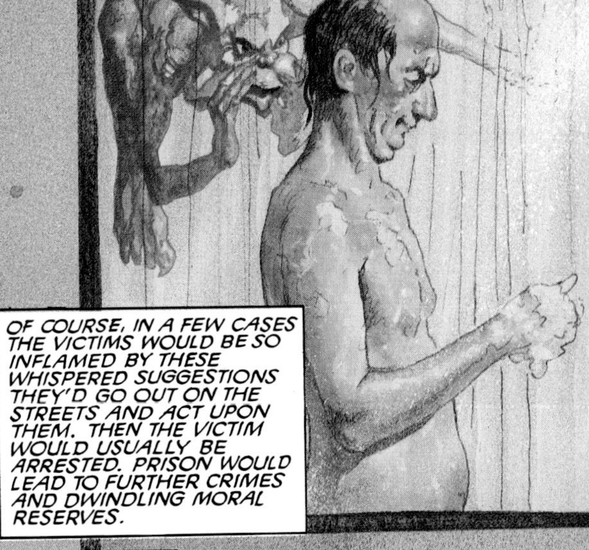

OF COURSE, IN A FEW CASES THE VICTIMS WOULD BE SO INFLAMED BY THESE WHISPERED SUGGESTIONS THEY'D GO OUT ON THE STREETS AND ACT UPON THEM. THEN THE VICTIM WOULD USUALLY BE ARRESTED. PRISON WOULD LEAD TO FURTHER CRIMES AND DWINDLING MORAL RESERVES.

ONE WAY OR ANOTHER INSANITY WOULD WIN OUT.

EXCEPT THAT FOR SOME REASON THIS RULE DID NOT APPLY TO POLO; HE WAS UNPERTURBABLE.

INDEED, THE WAY THINGS WERE GOING THE YATTERING WOULD BE THE ONE TO BREAK.

IT WAS TIRED; SO VERY TIRED.

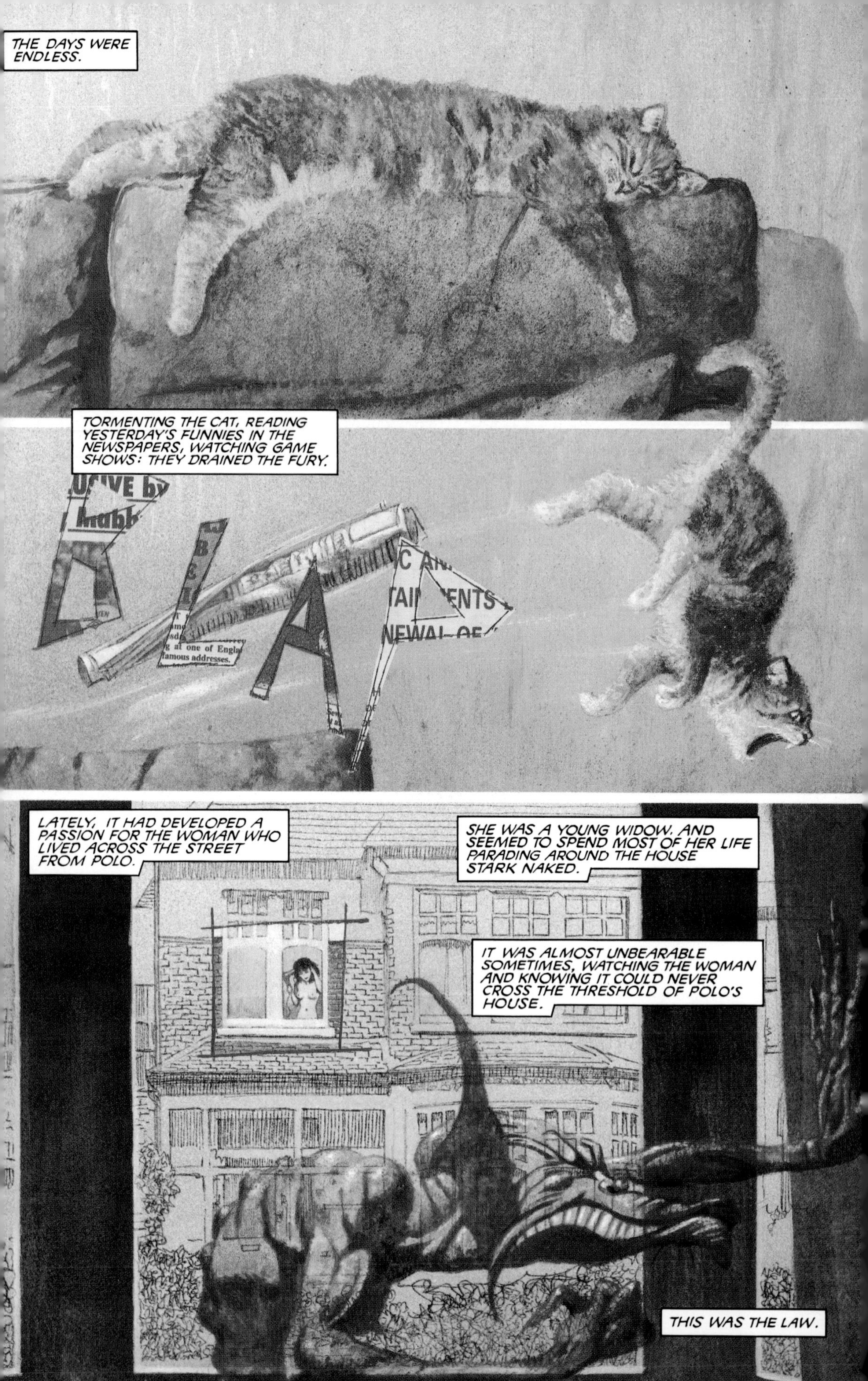
THE DAYS WERE ENDLESS.
TORMENTING THE CAT, READING YESTERDAY'S FUNNIES IN THE NEWSPAPERS, WATCHING GAME SHOWS: THEY DRAINED THE FURY.
LATELY, IT HAD DEVELOPED A PASSION FOR THE WOMAN WHO LIVED ACROSS THE STREET FROM POLO.
SHE WAS A YOUNG WIDOW. AND SEEMED TO SPEND MOST OF HER LIFE PARADING AROUND THE HOUSE STARK NAKED.
IT WAS ALMOST UNBEARABLE SOMETIMES, WATCHING THE WOMAN AND KNOWING IT COULD NEVER CROSS THE THRESHOLD OF POLO'S HOUSE.
THIS WAS THE LAW.

THE LAW.

THE YATTERING WAS A MINOR DEMON, AND HIS SOUL CATCHING WAS STRICTLY CONFINED TO THE PERIMETERS OF THE VICTIM'S HOUSE. TO STEP OUTSIDE WAS TO RELINQUISH ALL POWERS OVER THE VICTIM: TO PUT ITSELF AT THE MERCY OF HUMANITY.

ALL JUNE, ALL JULY AND MOST OF AUGUST IT SWEATED IN ITS PRISON; ALL THROUGH THOSE HOT MONTHS JACK POLO MAINTAINED COMPLETE INDIFFERENCE TO THE YATTERING'S ATTACKS.

IT WAS DEEPLY EMBARRASSING, AND IT WAS GRADUALLY DESTROYING THE DEMON'S SELF-CONFIDENCE, SEEING THIS BLAND VICTIM SURVIVE EVERY TRIAL AND TRICK ATTEMPTED ON HIM.

THE YATTERING WEPT.

THE YATTERING SCREAMED.

IN A FIT OF UNCONTROLLABLE ANGUISH, IT BOILED THE WATER IN THE AQUARIUM, POACHING THE GOLDFISH.

POLO HEARD NOTHING. SAW NOTHING.

AT LAST, IN LATE SEPTEMBER, THE YATTERING BROKE ONE OF THE FIRST RULES OF ITS CONDITION, AND APPEALED DIRECTLY TO ITS MASTERS.

AUTUMN IS HELL'S SEASON, AND THE DEMONS OF HIGHER DENOMINATIONS WERE FEELING BENIGN. THEY CONDESCENDED TO SPEAK TO THEIR CREATURE.

WHAT DO YOU WANT?

IT WAS BEELZEBUB, HIS VOICE BLACKENING THE AIR IN THE LOUNGE.

THIS MAN...

YES?

THIS POLO...

YES?

I AM NOT WITHOUT ISSUE UPON HIM. I CAN'T GET PANIC UPON HIM, I CAN'T BREED FEAR OR EVEN MILD CONCERN UPON HIM. I AM STERILE, LORD OF THE FLIES, AND I WISH TO BE PUT OUT OF MY MISERY.

YOU WANT WHAT?

I... WANT TO DIE.

YOU CANNOT DIE.

FROM THIS WORLD. JUST DIE FROM THIS WORLD. FADE AWAY. BE REPLACED.

BUT I CAN'T BREAK HIM.

YOU MUST.

WHY?

BECAUSE WE TELL YOU TO.

BEELZEBUB ALWAYS USED THE ROYAL "WE," THOUGH HE WAS UNQUALIFIED TO DO SO.

LET ME AT LEAST KNOW WHY I'M IN THIS HOUSE. WHAT IS HE? NOTHING! HE IS NOTHING!

BEELZEBUB FOUND THIS RICH. HE LAUGHED, BUZZED, TRUMPETED.

JACK JOHNSON POLO IS THE CHILD OF A WORSHIPPER AT THE CHURCH OF LOST SALVATION. HE BELONGS TO US.

BUT WHY SHOULD YOU WANT HIM? HE'S SO DULL.

WE WANT HIM BECAUSE HIS SOUL WAS PROMISED TO US, AND HIS MOTHER DID NOT DELIVER IT, OR HERSELF. SHE CHEATED US. SHE DIED IN THE ARMS OF A PRIEST, AND WAS SAFELY ESCORTED TO...
THE WORD THAT FOLLOWED WAS ANATHEMA. THE LORD OF THE FLIES COULD BARELY BRING HIMSELF TO PRONOUNCE IT.
...HEAVEN.
INFINITE LOSS WAS IN THE LORD'S VOICE.

HEAVEN.
THE YATTERING DID NOT QUITE KNOW WHAT WAS MEANT BY THE WORD.
POLO IS TO BE HOUNDED IN THE NAME OF THE OLD ONE AND PUNISHED FOR HIS CRIMES. NO TORMENT IS TOO PROFOUND FOR A FAMILY THAT HAS CHEATED US.
I'M TIRED. PLEASE. I BEG YOU.
CLAIM THIS MAN! OR YOU WILL SUFFER IN HIS PLACE!
WHERE IS YOUR PRIDE?
PRIDE, YATTERING, PRIDE.
THEN HE WAS GONE. THE LORD HAD SPOKEN.

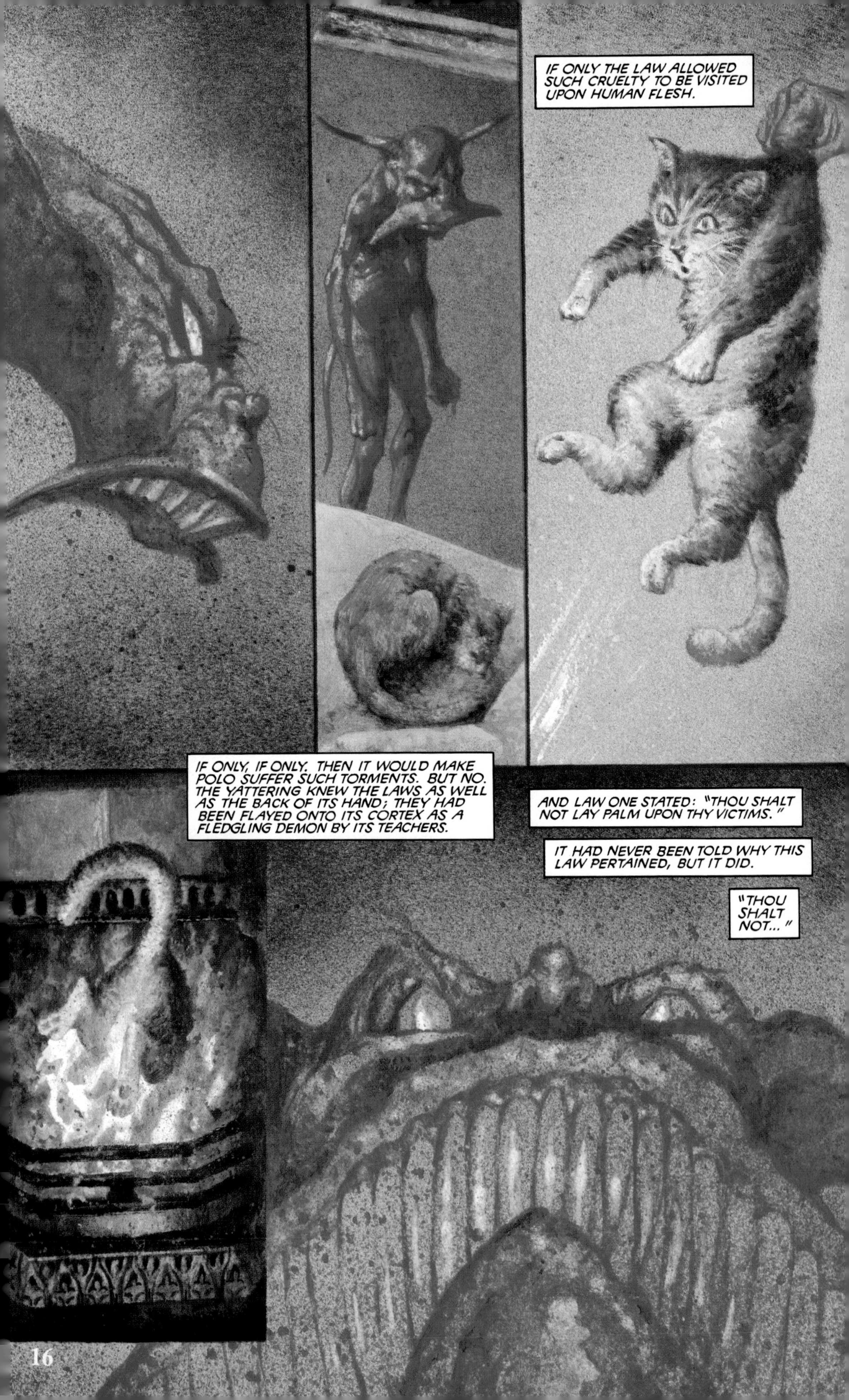
IF ONLY THE LAW ALLOWED SUCH CRUELTY TO BE VISITED UPON HUMAN FLESH.
IF ONLY, IF ONLY. THEN IT WOULD MAKE POLO SUFFER SUCH TORMENTS. BUT NO. THE YATTERING KNEW THE LAWS AS WELL AS THE BACK OF ITS HAND; THEY HAD BEEN FLAYED ONTO ITS CORTEX AS A FLEDGLING DEMON BY ITS TEACHERS.
AND LAW ONE STATED: "THOU SHALT NOT LAY PALM UPON THY VICTIMS."
IT HAD NEVER BEEN TOLD WHY THIS LAW PERTAINED, BUT IT DID.
"THOU SHALT NOT..."

SO THE WHOLE PAINFUL PROCESS CONTINUED. DAY IN, DAY OUT, AND STILL THE MAN SHOWED NO SIGN OF YIELDING.
POLO BROUGHT HOME A NEW CAT TO REPLACE HIS TREASURED FREDDY (NOW ASH).

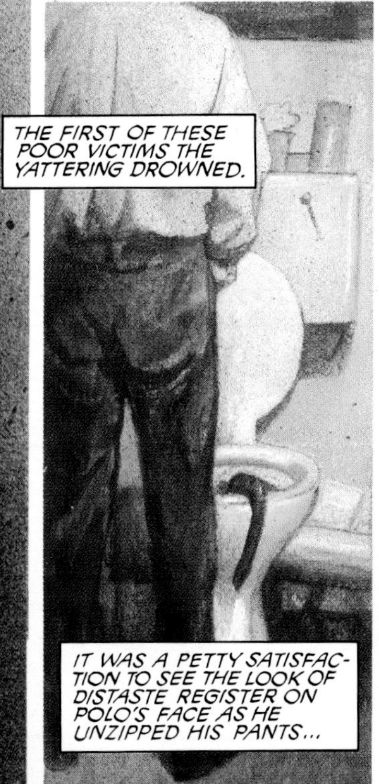

THE FIRST OF THESE POOR VICTIMS THE YATTERING DROWNED.
IT WAS A PETTY SATISFACTION TO SEE THE LOOK OF DISTASTE REGISTER ON POLO'S FACE AS HE UNZIPPED HIS PANTS...

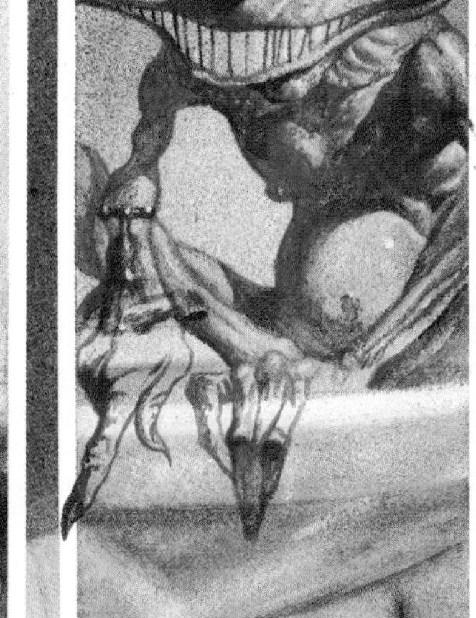

... BUT A SATISFACTION IT WAS.

BUT ANY PLEASURE THE YATTERING TOOK IN JACK'S DISCOMFITURE WAS CANCELLED OUT BY THE BLITHELY EFFICIENT WAY IN WHICH THE MAN DEALT WITH THE DEAD CAT, HOISTING THE BUNDLE OF SOAKING FUR OUT OF THE BOWL, WRAPPING IT IN A TOWEL...

... AND BURYING IT WITH SCARCELY A MURMUR.

THE THIRD CAT THAT POLO BROUGHT HOME WAS WISE TO THE INVISIBLE PRESENCE OF THE DEMON FROM THE START.
THIS WAS INDEED AN ENTERTAININ WEEK IN MID-NOVEMBER. LIFE FOR THE YATTERING BECAME ALMOST INTERESTING WHEN IT PLAYED CAT AND MOUSE WITH FREDDY III.
FREDDY PLAYED THE MOUS
CATS NOT BEING ESPECIALLY BRIGHT ANIMALS THE GAME WAS SCARCELY A GREAT INTELLECTUAL CHALLENGE, BUT IT MADE A CHANGE IN THE ENDLESS DAYS OF WAITING, HAUNTING AND FAILING.
AT LEAST IT ACCEPTE THE YATTERING'S PRESENCE.

EVENTUALLY, HOWEVER, IN A FILTHY MOOD (CAUSED BY THE REMARRIAGE OF THE YATTERING'S NAKED WIDOW) THE DEMON LOST ITS TEMPER WITH THE CAT.
IT WAS SHARPENING ITS NAILS ON THE NYLON CARPET, CLAWING AND SCRATCHING AT THE PILE FOR HOURS ON END.
Scri
Skr
Scritch
Scritch
skratch
Scritch
Skratch
THE NOISE PUT THE DEMON'S METAPHYSICAL TEETH ON EDGE. SCRATCHING AND CLAWING, SCRATCHING AND CLAWING.
Scritch
Skrat

THE EFFECT WAS SPECTACULAR. THE RESULTS GROSS.
CAT-BRAIN...
CAT-FUR...
CAT-GUT EVERYWHERE.

DAMN DOGS. DAMN, DAMN DOGS.

THERE WAS AN ANGER IN HIS VOICE. YES. ANGER. THE MAN WAS UPSET; THERE WAS CLEAR EVIDENCE OF EMOTION ON HIS FACE.

POLO JUST CLEANED UP THE CAT.

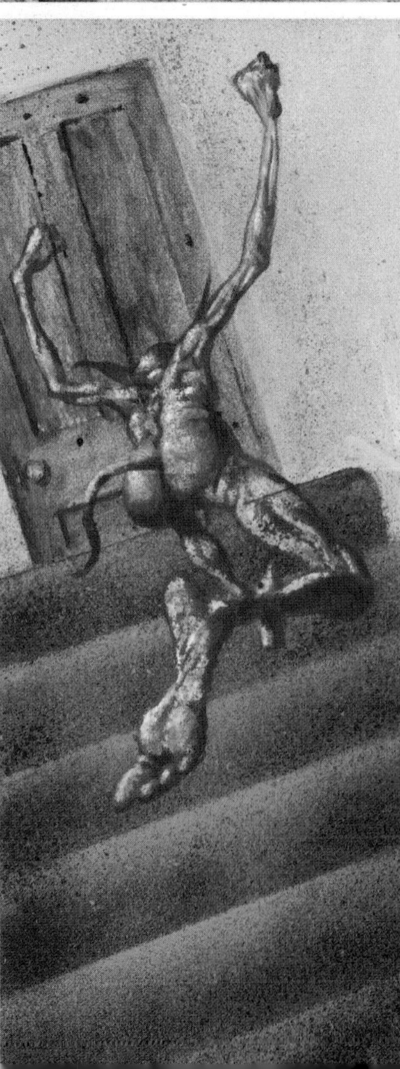

THE DEMON WAS UTTERLY STUMPED. IF THE MAN COULD NOT RAISE MORE THAN A FLICKER OF CONCERN WHEN HIS CAT EXPLODED IN THE LIVING-ROOM, WHAT CHANCE HAD IT GOT OF EVER BREAKING THE BASTARD?
THERE WAS ONE LAST OPPORTUNITY.
IT WAS APPROACHING CHRIST'S MASS, AND JACK'S CHILDREN WOULD BE COMING HOME TO THE BOSOM OF THE FAMILY. PERHAPS THEY COULD CONVINCE HIM THAT ALL WAS NOT WELL WITH THE WORLD; PERHAPS THEY COULD GET THEIR FINGERNAILS UNDER HIS FLAWLESS INDIFFERENCE, AND BEGIN TO BREAK HIM DOWN.
YES, PERHAPS.
HOPING AGAINST HOPE, THE YATTERING SAT OUT THE WEEKS TO LATE DECEMBER PEACEFULLY, PLANNING ITS ATTACKS WITH ALL THE IMAGINATIVE MALICE IT COULD MUSTER.
MEANWHILE, JACK'S LIFE SAUNTERED ON. HE SEEMED TO LIVE APART FROM HIS EXPERIENCE, LIVING HIS LIFE AS AN AUTHOR MIGHT WRITE A PREPOSTEROUS STORY, NEVER INVOLVING HIMSELF IN THE NARRATIVE TOO DEEPLY.
IN SEVERAL SIGNIFICANT WAYS, HOWEVER, POLO SHOWED HIS ENTHUSIASM FOR THE COMING HOLIDAY. HE CLEARED A ROOM FOR HIS DAUGHTERS IMMACULATELY. HE MADE THEIR BED WITH SWEET SMELLING LINEN. HE CLEANED EVERY SPECK OF CAT'S BLOOD OUT OF THE CARPET. HE EVEN SET UP A CHRISTMAS TREE, HUNG WITH IRIDESCENT BALLS AND PRESENTS.

ONCE IN A WHILE, AS HE WENT ABOUT THE PREPARATIONS, JACK THOUGHT OF THE GAME HE WAS PLAYING, AND QUIETLY CALCULATED THE ODDS AGAINST HIM.
IN THE DAYS TO COME HE WOULD HAVE TO MEASURE NOT ONLY HIS OWN SUFFERING, BUT THAT OF HIS DAUGHTERS, AGAINST THE POSSIBLE VICTORY.
AND ALWAYS, WHEN HE MADE THESE CALCULATIONS, THE CHANCE OF VICTORY SEEMED TO OUTWEIGH THE RISKS.
SO HE CONTINUED TO WRITE HIS LIFE, AND WAITED.
IT WAS POSSIBLE, FOR A BRIEF TIME, TO BELIEVE IN PEACE ON EARTH.

LATE IN THE EVENING OF THE TWENTY-THIRD OF DECEMBER THE DAUGHTERS ARRIVED IN A FLURRY OF CASES AND KISSES.
FROM ITS VANTAGE POINT ON THE LANDING THE YATTERING VIEWED THE YOUNG WOMEN BALEFULLY.
THE YOUNGEST, AMANDA, DIDN'T LOOK LIKE IDEAL MATERIAL IN WHICH TO INDUCE A BREAK-DOWN. IN FACT, SHE LOOKED DANGEROUS.
GINA FOLLOWED. A SMOOTHLY POLISHED WOMAN OF THE WORLD AND TWENTY-FOUR, SHE LOOKED EVERY BIT AS INTIMIDATING AS HER YOUNGER SISTER.

WITHIN THE SPACE OF A FEW HOURS THE DRAB HOUSE WAS REPAINTED WITH LIGHT, AND FUN, AND LOVE.
IT MADE THE YATTERING SICK.

SICK AND WHIMPERING, THE YATTERING RAN TO THE ATTIC TO BLOCK OUT THE DIN OF AFFECTION, BUT THE SHOCK-WAVES ENVELOPED IT.

ALL IT COULD DO WAS HIDE, AND LISTEN, AND REFINE ITS REVENGE.

JACK WAS PLEASED TO HAVE HIS BEAUTIES HOME. AMANDA SO FULL OF OPINIONS, AND SO STRONG, LIKE HER MOTHER. GINA MORE LIKE HIS MOTHER: POISED, PERCEPTIVE.

HE WAS SO HAPPY IN THEIR PRESENCE HE COULD HAVE WEPT; AND HERE HE WAS, THE PROUD FATHER, PUTTING THEM BOTH AT SUCH RISK.

BUT WHAT WAS THE ALTERNATIVE? IF HE HAD CANCELLED THE CHRISTMAS CELEBRATIONS, IT WOULD HAVE LOOKED HIGHLY SUSPICIOUS.

IT MIGHT EVEN HAVE SPOILED HIS WHOLE STRATEGY, WAKENING THE ENEMY TO THE TRICK THAT WAS BEING PLAYED.

NO; HE MUST SIT TIGHT. PLAY DUMB, THE WAY THE ENEMY HAD COME TO EXPECT HIM TO BE.

THE TIME WOULD COME FOR ACTION

AT 3:15 ON CHRISTMAS MORNING THE YATTERING OPENED HOSTILITIES.
A PALTRY PERFORMANCE AT BEST, BUT IT HAD THE INTENDED EFFECT.
GINA.
HMGFHM...
GINA!
WHAT?
THERE'S SOMEBODY UNDER THE BED.
THERE'S NOTHING THERE--
THERE'S SOMETHING IN THE ROOM WITH US, GINA. I'M SURE OF IT.
NO. IT'S EMPTY.

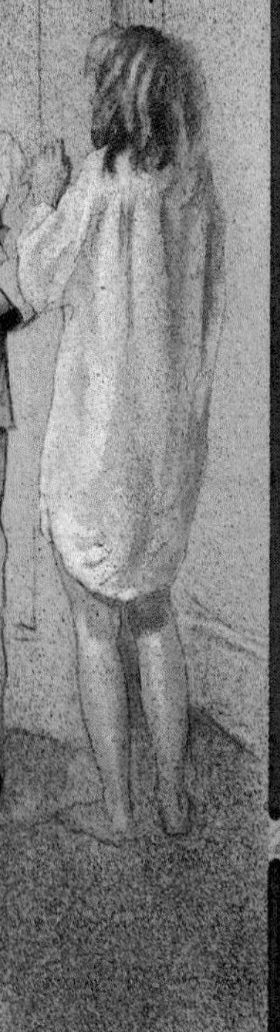
WHAT'S ALL THE NOISE?
THERE'S SOMETHING IN THE HOUSE, DADDY. I WAS THROWN OUT OF BED.

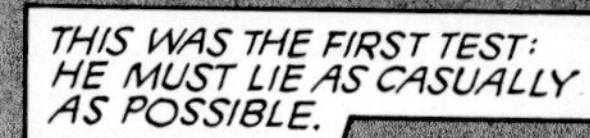

THIS WAS THE FIRST TEST: HE MUST LIE AS CASUALLY AS POSSIBLE.
LOOKS LIKE YOU'VE BEEN HAVING NIGHTMARES, BEAUTY.
THERE WAS SOMETHING UNDER THE BED.

THERE'S NOBODY HERE NOW.
BUT I FELT IT.
WELL, I'LL CHECK THE REST OF THE HOUSE. YOU TWO STAY HERE, JUST IN CASE.

SUBSIDENCE.

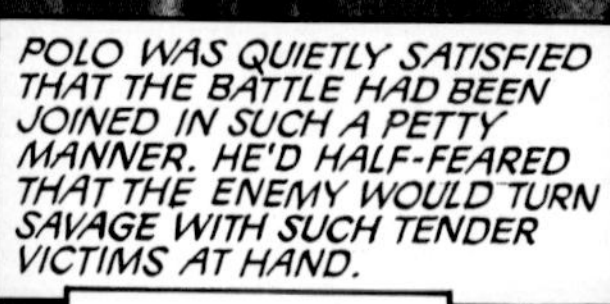
POLO WAS QUIETLY SATISFIED THAT THE BATTLE HAD BEEN JOINED IN SUCH A PETTY MANNER. HE'D HALF-FEARED THAT THE ENEMY WOULD TURN SAVAGE WITH SUCH TENDER VICTIMS AT HAND.
BUT NO; HE'D JUDGED THE MIND OF THE CREATURE QUITE ACCURATELY.

IT WAS ONE OF THE LOWER ORDERS. POWERFUL, BUT SLOW. CAPABLE OF BEING INVEIGLED BEYOND THE LIMITS OF ITS CONTROL.

HE TRAIPSED THROUGH THE ENTIRE HOUSE SEARCHING DUTIFULLY, THEN RETURNED TO HIS DAUGHTERS.
AMANDA LOOKED SMALL AND PALE, NOT THE TWENTY-TWO YEAR OLD WOMAN SHE WAS, BUT A CHILD AGAIN.
NOTHING DOING. IT'S CHRISTMAS MORNING AND ALL THROUGH THE HOUSE--

NOTHING WAS STIRRING; NOT EVEN A MOUSE.

NOT EVEN A MOUSE, BEAUTY.

SHIT.

HE NEEDED SOME SLEEP, BUT QUITE CLEARLY THE YATTERING HAD NO INTENTION OF LETTING THEM ALONE JUST YET.

QUE SERÁ, SERÁ.
THE HOUSE IS SINKING A LITTLE ON THE LEFT SIDE, YOU KNOW. IT HAS BEEN FOR YEARS.
SUBSIDENCE... WOULD NOT THROW ME OUT OF BED.
WELL, MAYBE IT WAS SANTA CLAUS.
WHAT ELSE CAN IT BE? THE ONLY OTHER EXPLANA-TION...
POLO WAS ALMOST ELATED BY SKIMMING SO CLOSE TO THE TRUTH.
...THE ONLY OTHER POSSIBLE EXPLANATION IS TOO PREPOSTEROUS FOR WORDS.
IT WAS AN EXQUISITE IRONY, DENYING THE EXISTENCE OF THE INVISIBLE WORLD IN THE FULL KNOWLEDGE THAT EVEN NOW IT BREATHED VENGEFULLY DOWN HIS NECK.
YOU MEAN POLTERGEIST?
I MEAN ANY-THING THAT GOES BANG IN THE NIGHT. BUT WE'RE GROWN-UP PEOPLE, AREN'T WE? WE DON'T BELIEVE IN BOGEYMEN.
NO, I DON'T, BUT I DON'T BELIEVE THE HOUSE IS SUBSIDING, EITHER.
WELL, IT'LL HAVE TO DO FOR NOW; CHRISTMAS STARTS HERE. WE DON'T WANT TO SPOIL IT TALKING ABOUT GREMLINS, NOW DO WE?

GREMLIN. THAT SURELY BIT DEEP. TO CALL A HELL-SPAWN A GREMLIN.
THERE WOULD BE TIME YET TO BEAT THAT ATHEISTIC SMILE OFF JACK POLO'S SMOOTH, FAT FACE. TIME APLENTY. NO HALF-MEASURES FROM NOW ON. NO SUBTLETY. IT WOULD BE AN ALL-OUT ATTACK.
LET THERE BE BLOOD. LET THERE BE AGONY.
THEY'D ALL BREAK.

CHRISTMAS.
THROUGH THE HOUSE DRIFTED THE SOUND OF KING'S COLLEGE CHOIR, "O LITTLE TOWN OF BETHLEHEM, HOW STILL WE SEE THEE LIE..."
THE PRESENTS HAD BEEN OPENED, THE G AND T's WERE BEING DOWNED, THE HOUSE WAS ONE WARM EMBRACE FROM ROOF TO CELLAR.
A SUDDEN CHILL PERMEATED THE HEAT AND STEAM, MAKING AMANDA SHIVER.
MAYBE SHE WAS CATCHING SOMETHING.
SHE FELT THE STARE QUITE CLEARLY. SHE TURNED.
NOBODY, NOTHING.
AMANDA CONTINUED TO WASH THE BRUSSELS SPROUTS, CUTTING INTO ONE WITH A WORM CURLED IN THE MIDDLE. SHE DROWNED IT.
THE CHOIR SANG ON.
IN THE LIVING ROOM, JACK WAS LAUGHING WITH GINA ABOUT SOMETHING.
THEN, A NOISE. A BEATING OF SOMEBODY'S FISTS AGAINST THE DOOR.
LIKE SOMETHING LOCKED IN ONE OF THE CUPBOARDS, DESPERATE TO ESCAPE. A CAT CAUGHT IN A BOX, OR A...
...BIRD.
IT WAS COMING FROM THE OVEN.
SKRKK

AMANDA'S STOMACH TURNED, AS SHE BEGAN TO IMAGINE THE WORST. HAD SHE LOCKED SOMETHING IN THE OVEN WHEN SHE PUT IN THE TURKEY?
KA-TUMP
KA-TINK
SHE HAD VISIONS OF A BASTED CAT LEAPING OUT AT HER, ITS FUR BURNED OFF, ITS FLESH HALF-COOKED.
THERE'S SOMETHING IN THE OVEN.
AS IF HE NEEDED TO BE TOLD. THE OVEN WAS IN A FRENZY.
KA-SPING
KA-SPANG
THIS WAS NEW, THOUGHT POLO, YOU'RE BETTER THAN I JUDGED YOU TO BE. THIS IS CLEVER. THIS IS ORIGINAL.
TUMP
THE HANDLE WAS SLIPPERY WITH HEAT AND GREASE.

HEADLESS, OOZING STUFFING AND ONIONS, IT FLOPPED AROUND AS THOUGH NOBODY HAD TOLD THE DAMN THING THAT IT WAS DEAD.

JACK CURSED HIS CONFIDENCE.

THE OPPOSITION HAD MORE UP ITS SLEEVE THAN HE'D GUESSED.

SPLORT
SPLIP
SPLAP
SPLUP

THE RADIO WAS STILL CROONING CAROLS WHICH BLOTTED OUT THE NOISE OF THE BIRD, BUT THEIR PROMISES OF GOOD-WILL SEEMED SMALL COMFORT.
WHAT WAS THAT?
I DON'T KNOW WHAT IT WAS.
MASS HYSTERIA?
GINA'S DISPLEASURE WAS PLAIN. HER FATHER HAD A SECRET.
HER FATHER KNEW WHAT WAS GOING ON IN THE HOUSE, BUT HE WAS REFUSING TO COUGH UP FOR SOME REASON.
WHO DO I CALL--THE POLICE OR AN EXORCIST?
NEITHER.
FOR GOD'S SAKE...
THERE'S NOTHING GOING ON, GINA. REALLY.
THIS WAS WAR.
JACK WAS AFRAID.
THE HOUSE WAS SUDDENLY A PRISON. THE GAME WAS SUDDENLY LETHAL. THE ENEMY, INSTEAD OF PLAYING FOOLISH GAMES, MEANT HARM.
REAL HARM TO THEM ALL.
THE CAROLS ON THE RADIO HA
WITHERED INTO A SERMON O
GOD'S BENEDICTIONS.

WHAT HAD BEEN SWEET WAS SOUR AND DANGEROUS. POLO WANTED TO EXPLAIN WHAT WAS GOING ON.

BUT THE THING MUST BE THERE, HE KNEW, GLOATING.

POLO WAS WRONG.

THE YATTERING HAD RETIRED TO THE ATTIC, WELL-SATISFIED WITH ITS ENDEAVORS. THE BIRD, IT FELT, HAD BEEN A STROKE OF GENIUS. NOW IT COULD REST A WHILE, PLAY AND RECUPERATE.

LET THE ENEMIES TATTER THEMSELVES IN ANTICIPATION. THEN, IN ITS OWN GOOD TIME, IT WOULD DELIVER THE COUP DE GRACE.

IT WONDERED IF ANY OF THE INSPECTORS HAD SEEN HIS WORK WITH THE TURKEY. MAYBE THEY WOULD BE IMPRESSED ENOUGH BY THE YATTERING'S ORIGINALITY TO IMPROVE ITS JOB PROSPECTS.

SURELY IT HADN'T GONE THROUGH ALL THOSE YEARS OF TRAINING SIMPLY TO CHASE HALF-WITTED IMBECILES LIKE POLO. THERE MUST BE SOMETING MORE CHALLENGING AVAILABLE THAN THAT.

IT FELT VICTORY IN ITS HELL-BORN BONES; AND IT WAS A GOOD FEELING.

THE PURSUIT OF POLO WOULD SURELY GAIN MOMENTUM NOW. HIS DAUGHTERS WOULD CONVINCE HIM THAT THERE WAS SOMETHING TERRIBLE AFOOT.
HE WOULD CRACK. HE WOULD CRUMBLE.
MAYBE HE'D GO CLASSICALL MAD: TEAR OUT HIS HAIR, RIP OFF HIS CLOTHES, SMEAR HIMSELF WITH HIS OWN EXCREMENT.
OH YES, VICTORY WAS CLOSE. AND WOULDN'T ITS MASTERS BE LOVING, THEN? WOULDN'T IT BE SHOWERED WITH PRAISE AND POWER?
ONE MORE MANIFESTATION WAS ALL THAT WAS REQUIRED. ONE FINAL, INSPIRED INTER-VENTION, AND POLO WOULD BE SO MUCH BLUBBERING FLESH.
THE GHERKIN IMPORTER WASN'T IN THE ROOM.
WASN'T THAT HIS FOOTSTEP ON THE STAIR?
YES, HE WAS GOING UP-STAIRS TO RELIEVE HIS BRANDY-FULL BLADDER.
IDEAL TIMING

IN HER SLEEP AMANDA DREAMED SOMETHING DARK FLITTING ACROSS HER VISION, SOMETHING MALIGN, SOMETHING THAT TASTED BITTER IN HER MOUTH.

THE SILVER BALLS ON THE TREE WERE ROCKING GENTLY. NOT JUST THE BALLS, THE TINSEL AND THE BRANCHES TOO.
TINKEL
THE TREE BEGAN TO SPIN.
CHRIST... JESUS CHRIST.
THE TREE PICKED UP MOMENTUM.

FATHER!
POLO BURST INTO THE LIVING ROOM HALF EXPECTING ALL THE HOSTS OF HELL TO BE THERE, DOG-HEADED, DANCING WITH HIS BEAUTIES.
BUT NO. IT WAS THE TREE THAT WAS WHINING, WHINING LIKE A PACK OF DOGS, AS IT SPUN AND SPUN.
THE AIR STANK OF SINGED PLASTIC AND PINE-SAP.
GET OUT OF HERE!

COME ON... GET OUT!!

THE POKERS BESIDE THE FIRE. THE CUSHIONS. THE ORNAMENTS. EACH OBJECT ADDED ITS OWN SINGULAR NOTE TO THE ORCHESTRATION OF WHINES WHICH WERE BUILDING UP, SECOND BY SECOND, TO A DEAFENING PITCH.
JACK COULD SEE THE ENEMY, IN HIS MIND'S EYE, RACING BETWEEN THE OBJECTS LIKE A JUGGLER SPINNING PLATES ON A STICK, TRYING TO KEEP THEM ALL MOVING AT ONCE. IT MUST BE EXHAUSTING WORK, HE THOUGHT. THE DEMON WAS PROBABLY CLOSE TO COLLAPSE. IT COULDN'T BE THINKING STRAIGHT. OVER-EXCITED. IMPULSIVE... VULNERABLE.
THIS MUST BE THE MOMENT, IF EVER THERE WAS A MOMENT, TO JOIN BATTLE AT LAST. TO FACE THE THING, DEFY IT, AND TRAP IT.

FOR ITS PART, THE YATTERING WAS ENJOYING THE ORGY OF DESTRUCTION. IT FLUNG EVERY MOVABLE OBJECT INTO THE FRAY, SET EVERYTHING SPINNING. IT WATCHED WITH SATISFACTION.
SURELY HE WAS NEARLY MAD, WASN'T HE?

LIKE A MAN IN A CLOUD OF LOCUST POLO RAN AROUND THE ROOM, BRINGING DOWN HIS FAVORITE BOOKS IN A WELTER OF FLUTTERING PAGES...
...SMASHING WHIRLING DRESDEN, SHATTERING LAMPS. A LITTER OF BROKEN POSSESSIONS SWAMPED THE FLOOR, SOME OF IT TWITCHING AS LIFE WENT OUT OF THE FRAGMENTS. BUT, FOR EVERY OBJECT BROUGHT DOWN, THERE WERE A DOZEN STILL SPINNING, STILL WHINING.
POLO COULD HEAR GINA AT THE DOOR, YELLING TO HIM TO GET OUT, TO LEAVE IT ALONE.
BUT IT WAS SO ENJOYABLE, PLAYING AGAINST THE ENEMY MORE DIRECTLY THAN HE'D EVER ALLOWED HIMSELF BEFORE. HE DIDN'T WANT TO GIVE UP. HE WANTED THE DEMON TO SHOW ITSELF, TO BE KNOWN, TO BE RECOGNIZED.
HE WANTED CONFIRMATION WITH THE OLD ONE'S EMISSARY ONCE AND FOR ALL.
THEN THE TREE EXPLODED.

THE ROOM WAS SO THICK WITH A BARRAGE OF SHARDS IT WAS LIKE A FOG. GINA WAS CROUCHING AT THE DOOR, URGING HIM TO HURRY.
AS JACK REACHED THE DOOR, AND FELT GINA'S ARMS AROUND HIM, HE SWORE HE COULD HEAR LAUGHTER FROM THE LIVING ROOM. TANGIBLE, AUDIBLE LAUGHTER, RICH AND SATISFIED.
WHAT IS IT?
POLTERGEIST? GHOST?
MOTHER'S GHOST?!

THE THOUGHT OF HIS DEAD WIFE BEING RESPONSIBLE FOR SUCH WHOLESALE DESTRUCTION STRUCK JACK AS FUNNY.
AMANDA WAS HALF SMILING. GOOD, HE THOUGHT, SHE'S COMING OUT OF IT.
THEN HE MET THE VACANT LOOK IN HER EYES AND THE TRUTH DAWNED. SHE'D BROKEN, HER SANITY HAD TAKEN REFUGE WHERE THIS FANTASTIQUE COULDN'T GET AT IT.
WHAT'S IN THERE?!
I DON'T KNOW.
YOU DO KNOW.
NO.
YOU'RE LYING.
I THINK...
I THINK... I SHALL GO FOR A WALK.

THE AIR IN THE HALLWAY WAS ELECTRIC WITH UNSEEN PRESENCES. IT WAS VERY CLOSE TO HIM, INVISIBLE AS EVER, BUT CLOSE.
THIS WAS THE MOST DANGEROUS TIME. HE MUSTN'T LOSE HIS NERVE NOW. HE MUST WALK AS THOUGH NOTHING HAD HAPPENED; HE MUST LEAVE AMANDA BE, LEAVE EXPLANATIONS UNTIL IT WAS ALL OVER AND DONE.

WALK ???!!
YES... WALK... I NEED SOME FRESH AIR.
YOU CAN'T LEAVE US HERE.
I'LL FIND SOMEBODY TO HELP US CLEAR UP.
BUT MANDY... !

SHE'LL GET OVER IT. LEAVE HER BE.
THAT WAS HARD. THAT WA ALMOST UNFORGIVABLE. BUT IT WAS SAID NOW.
YOU CAN'T JUST LEAVE! ARE YOU OUT OF YOUR MIND?
I NEED TH AIR. I'LL JU GO FOR A MOMENT.

NO
NO
NO
NO

IT WAS WITH HIM, POLO COULD FEEL IT. SO ANGRY NOW, SO READY TO TWIST OFF HIS HEAD.
EXCEPT THAT IT WASN'T ALLOWED, EVER, TO TOUCH HIM. BUT POLO COULD FEEL ITS RESENTMENT LIKE A PHYSICAL PRESENCE.
YOU SONOFABITCH, LOOK AT MANDY! SHE'S LOST HER MIND!
SHE'LL BE ALL RIGHT.
NO, HE MUSTN'T LOOK AT MANDY. IF HE LOOKED AT MANDY HE MIGHT WEEP, HE'D BREAK DOWN AS THE THING WANTED HIM TO, THEN EVERYTHING WOULD BE LOST.
POLO REACHED FOR THE DOOR KNOB. THE DEMON BOLTED THE DOOR QUICKLY, LOUDLY. NO TEMPER LEFT FOR PRETENSE NOW.
JACK, KEEPING HIS MOVEMENTS AS EVEN AS POSSIBLE, UNBOLTED THE DOOR.
IT WAS THRILLING, THIS GAME; IT WAS ALSO TERRIFYING. IF HE PUSHED TOO FAR SURELY THE DEMON'S FRUSTRATION WOULD OVERRIDE ITS LESSONS.
JACK WONDERED HOW LONG HE COULD KEEP THIS UP FOR. SOMEHOW HE HAD TO GET OUTSIDE; HE HAD TO COAX IT OVER THE THRESHOLD. ONE STEP WAS ALL THE LAW REQUIRED, ACCORDING TO HIS RESEARCHES.
ONE SIMPLE STEP.
UNBOLTED. BOLTED. UNBOLTED. BOLTED.

GINA DIDN'T UNDERSTAND WHAT SHE WAS SEEING, BUT IT WAS OBVIOUS HER FATHER WAS DOING BATTLE WITH SOMEONE, OR SOMETHING.
DADDY...
SHUT UP.
INEXPLICABLY, SHE RETURNED THE SMILE. IT WAS GRIM, BUT GENUINE. WHATEVER WAS AT ISSUE HERE, SHE LOVED HIM.
POLO MADE A BREAK FOR THE BACK DOOR.

THE DEMON WAS THREE PACES AHEAD OF POLO, SCOOTING THROUGH THE HOUSE LIKE A SPRINTER.
KLIK
THE KEY WAS TURNED IN THE LOCK...
...THEN CRUSHED TO DUST IN THE AIR.

IT AVOIDED A COLLISION ONLY BY THE MOST BALLETIC OF MANEUVERS.
THAT WOULD BE FATAL INDEED; TO TOUCH THE MAN IN THE HEAT OF THE MOMENT.
WISE TO HER FATHER'S STRATEGY, GINA HAD UNBOLTED THE DOOR WHILE THE YATTERING AND JACK FOUGHT AT THE BACK DOOR.
JACK HAD PRAYED SHE'D TAKE THE OPPORTUNITY.
SHE HAD.

ALL THE CREATURE WANTED AT THAT MOMENT, BEYOND ANY OTHER DREAM, WAS TO TAKE THIS HUMAN'S SKULL BETWEEN ITS PALMS AND MAKE NON-SENSE OF IT. CRUSH IT TO SMITHEREENS, AND POUR THE HOT THOUGHT OUT ONTO THE SNOW. TO BE DONE WITH JACK J. POLO, FOREVER, AND EVER.
WAS THAT SO MUCH TO ASK?
ESCAPING. ESCAPING.
THE YATTERING HOWLED, FORGETTING ITS YEARS OF TRAINING. EVERY LESSON IT HAD LEARNED, EVERY RULE OF BATTLE ENGRAVED IN ITS SKULL, WAS SUBMERGED BY THE SIMPLE DESIRE TO HAVE POLO'S LIFE.

KILL JACK POLO!
SOMEWHERE IN HELL, THE POWERS FELT THE SIN, AND KNEW THE WAR FOR JACK POLO'S SOUL WAS LOST.
JACK FELT IT TOO.
IT WAS COMING AFTER HIM! THE THING HAD BROKEN THE FIRST RULE OF ITS EXISTENCE. IT WAS FORFEIT.
QUE SERÁ SERÁ.
THE YATTERING COULD BEAR IT NO LONGER.

THE TOUCH WAS THE SECOND SIN; AND IT AGONIZED THE YATTERING BEYOND ENDURANCE. IT BAYED LIKE A BANSHEE AND REELED AWAY FROM THE CONTACT.
IT KNEW ITS MISTAKE. THE LESSONS IT HAD LEARNED WERE HURTLING BACK. IT KNEW THE PUNISHMENT TOO FOR LEAVING THE HOUSE, FOR TOUCHING THE MAN.
IT WAS BOUND TO A NEW LORD, ENSLAVED TO THIS IDIOT- CREATURE STANDING OVER IT.
POLO HAD WON.

LIKE A PHOTOGRAPH DEVELOPING ON A SHEET OF PAPER, THE IMAGE OF THE FURY CAME CLEAR TO POLO'S EYES. THE LAW HAD TAKEN ITS TOLL.
THE YATTERING COULD NEVER HIDE FROM ITS MASTER AGAIN. THERE IT WAS, PLAIN TO POLO'S EYES IN ALL ITS CHARMLESS GLORY.
YOU BASTARD.
ITS ACCENT HAD AN AUSTRALIAN LILT.
YOU WILL NOT SPEAK UNLESS SPOKEN TO.
UNDERSTOOD?
YES.
YES, MISTER POLO.
YES, MISTER POLO.
YOU MAY STAND.

THEY'LL HAVE YOU YET.
WHO WILL?
YOU KNOW.
NAME THEM.
BEELZEBUB. THE POWERS. HELL ITSELF.
I DON'T THINK SO. NOT WITH YOU BOUND TO ME AS PROOF OF MY SKILLS. AREN'T I THE BETTER OF THEM?
AREN'T I?
YES. YES, YOU ARE THE BETTER OF THEM.
ARE YOU COLD?
YES.
THEN YOU NEED SOME EXERCISE. YOU BETTER GO BAC INTO THE HOUS AND START TIDYING.
NOTHING MORE? NO MIRACLES? NO HELEN OF TROY? NO FLYING?
THE THOUGHT OF FLYING ON A SNOW-SPLATTERED AFTERNOON LIKE THIS LEFT POLO COLD. HE WAS A MAN OF SIMPLE TASTES: ALL HE ASKED FOR IN LIFE WAS THE LOVE OF HIS CHILDREN, A PLEASANT HOME, AND A GOOD TRADING PLACE FOR GHERKINS.
NO FLYING.
AS THE YATTERING SLOUCHED DOWN THE PATH TOWARD THE HOUSE, IT SEEMED TO ALIGHT UPON A NEW PIECE OF MISCHIEF.
COULD I JUST SAY SOME-THING?
SPEAK.
IT'S ONLY FAIR THAT I INFORM YOU THAT IT'S CONSIDERED UNGODLY TO HAVE ANY CONTACT WITH THE LIKES OF ME. HERETICAL, EVEN.
IS THAT SO.
OH YES, PEOPLE HAVE BEEN BURNED FOR LESS.
NOT IN THIS DAY AND AGE.
BUT THE SERAPHIM WI SEE. AND THA MEANS YOU'L NEVER GO TO THAT PLACE.
WHAT PLACE?

THE YATTERING FUMBLED FOR THE SPECIAL WORD IT HAD HEARD BEELZEBUB USE.
HEAVEN.
THIS WAS THE CLEVEREST MANEUVER IT HAD ATTEMPTED; IT WAS JUGGLING THEOLOGY HERE.
THE CREATURE WAS PROBABLY TELLING THE TRUTH; ASSOCIATION WITH IT OR ITS LIKE WOULD NOT BE LOOKED UPON BENIGNLY BY THE HOST OF SAINTS AND ANGELS.
HE PROBABLY WAS FORBIDDEN ACCESS TO THE PLAINS OF PARADISE.
WELL, YOU KNOW WHAT I HAVE TO SAY ABOUT THAT, DON'T YOU?
NO, IT DIDN'T KNOW. THEN IT SAW WHAT POLO WAS DRIVING AT.
WHAT DO I SAY?
QUE SERÁ SERÁ.
KLIK

Merry Christmas

HOW SPOILERS BLEED
LOCKE RAISED HIS EYES TO THE TREES. THE WIND WAS MOVING IN THEM, AND THE COMMOTION OF THEIR LADEN BRANCHES SOUNDED LIKE THE RIVER IN FULL SPATE. ONE IMPERSONATION OF MANY. WHEN HE HAD FIRST COME TO THE JUNGLE, HE HAD BEEN AWED BY THE SHEER MULTIPLICITY OF BEAST AND BLOSSOM, THE RESTLESS PARADE OF LIFE. BUT HE HAD LEARNED BETTER. THIS BURGEONING DIVERSITY WAS A SHAM; THE JUNGLE PRETENDED ITSELF AN ARTLESS GARDEN . IT WAS NOT.
WHERE THE UNTUTORED TRESPASSER SAW ONLY A BRILLIANT SHOW OF NATURAL SPLENDOURS, LOCKE NOW RECOGNISED A SUBTLE CONSPIRACY AT WORK, IN WHICH EACH THING MIRRORED SOME OTHER THING.
H.ECTOR
ROUND AND ROUND IN A DIZZYING CIRCLE OF IMPERSONATIONS, A HALL OF MIRRORS WHICH CONFOUNDED THE SENSES AND WOULD, GIVEN TIME, ROT REASON ALTOGETHER.

LOCKE?
LOCKE, ARE YOU AWAKE?
WHAT DO YOU WANT?
I CAN'T SLEEP. I'VE BEEN THINKING. THE SUPPLY PLANE COMES IN FROM SANTAREM THE DAY AFTER TOMORROW. WE COULD BE BACK THERE IN A FEW HOURS, OUT OF ALL THIS.
I MEAN *PERMANENTLY*... AWAY.
PERMANENTLY?
I DON'T BELIEVE IN CURSES. DON'T THINK I DO. BUT YOU SAW CHERRICK'S BODY...WHAT HAPPENED TO HIM.
THERE'S A DISEASE--WHAT'S IT CALLED? WHEN THE BLOOD DOESN'T SET PROPERLY?
HEMOPHILIA. HE DIDN'T HAVE HEMOPHILIA AND WE BOTH KNOW IT. I'VE SEEN HIM CUT A MILLION TIMES. HE MENDED LIKE YOU OR I DO.
ALL RIGHT. THEN WHAT KILLED HIM?

YOU SAW THE WOUNDS BETTER THAN I DID, BUT IT SEEMED TO ME HIS SKIN JUST BROKE OPEN AS SOON AS HE WAS TOUCHED. MAYBE IT'S SOMETHING HE CAUGHT OFF THE INDIANS.
I DIDN'T TOUCH ANY OF THEM.
NEITHER DID I. BUT CHERRICK DID, REMEMBER?
LOCKE REMEMBERED; SCENES LIKE THAT WEREN'T EASY TO FORGET, TRY AS HE MIGHT.
I'M GOING BACK TO SANTAREM. I DON'T WANT THEM COMING, LOOKING FOR ME.
THEY'RE NOT GOING TO.
HOW DO YOU KNOW? WE SCREWED UP BACK THERE. WE COULD HAVE BRIBED THEM. GOT THEM OFF THE LAND SOME OTHER WAY.
I DOUBT IT. YOU HEARD WHAT TETELMAN SAID. ANCESTRAL TERRITORIES.
YOU CAN HAVE MY SHARE OF THE LAND. I WANT NO PART OF IT. I FEEL DIRTY. WE'RE SPOILERS, LOCKE.
IT'S YOUR FUNERAL.
I MEAN IT. I'M NOT LIKE YOU. NEVER REALLY HAD THE STOMACH FOR THIS KIND OF THING. WILL YOU BUY MY THIRD OFF ME?
DEPENDS ON THE PRICE.
WHATEVER YOU WANT TO GIVE. IT'S YOURS.

CONFESSIONAL OVER, STUMPF RETURNED TO HIS BED.
IT WOULD SOON BE LIGHT. ANOTHER JUNGLE DAWN.
HOW HE HATED THE PLACE. AT LEAST HE HADN'T TOUCHED ANY OF THE INDIANS; HADN'T EVEN BEEN WITHIN BREATHING DISTANCE OF THEM.
WHATEVER INFECTION THEY'D PASSED ON TO CHERRICK, HE COULD SURELY NOT BE TAINTED. IN LESS THAN FORTY-EIGHT HOURS HE WOULD BE AWAY TO SANTAREM, AND THEN ON TO SOME CITY, ANY CITY, WHERE THE TRIBE COULD NEVER FOLLOW.
HE'D ALREADY DONE HIS PENANCE, HADN'T HE?
STUMPF PRAYED, AND SLIPPED, BEFORE THE MONKEYS BEGAN TO CALL UP THE DAY, INTO A SPOILER'S SLEEP.

THEY HAD COME INTO THE INDIAN HAMLET AT NOON; THE SUN A BASILISK'S EYE.
IT WAS CHERRICK WHO FIRST SPOTTED THE CHILD.
AT FIRST THEY THOUGHT THE PLACE DESERTED. LOCKE AND CHERRICK HAD ADVANCED INTO THE COMPOUND, LEAVING THE DYSENTERY-RIDDEN STUMPF IN THE JEEP.

IF THERE WAS A FLICKER OF FEELING ON THEIR FACES, LOCKE COULD NOT READ IT. THESE PEOPLE WERE IMPOSSIBLE TO DECIPHER; DECEIT WAS THEIR ONLY SKILL.
WHAT ARE YOU DOING HERE? THIS IS OUR LAND.
THEY DON'T UNDERSTAND YOU.
GET THE KRAUT OUT HERE. LET HIM EXPLAIN IT TO THEM.
HE CAN'T MOVE.
GET HIM OUT HERE. I DON'T CARE IF HE'S SHAT HIS PANTS.
CHERRICK EASED AWAY, LEAVING LOCKE STANDING IN THE RING OF HUTS.
THERE WERE AT MOST TWO DOZEN INDIANS, DESCENDANTS OF THE GREAT PEOPLE THAT HAD ONCE ROAMED THE AMAZON BASIN IN THEIR TENS OF THOUSANDS.
NOW THOSE TRIBES WERE ALL BUT DECIMATED. THE FOREST IN WHICH THEY HAD PROSPERED FOR GENERATIONS WAS BEING LEVELLED AND BURNED; EIGHT-LANE HIGHWAYS WERE SPEEDING THROUGH THEIR HUNTING GROUNDS. ALL THEY HELD SACRED WAS BEING TRAMPLED AND TRESPASSED.
THEY WERE EXILES IN THEIR OWN LAND.
BUT STILL THEY DECLINED TO PAY HOMAGE TO THEIR NEW MASTERS, DESPITE THE RIFLES THEY BROUGHT.
ONLY DEATH WOULD CONVINCE THEM OF DEFEAT, LOCKE MUSED.

LOCKE WANTS YOU.
I CAN'T MOVE. I'M DYING--
LOCKE WANTS YOU DEAD OR ALIVE.
ALL RIGHT. HELP ME.
WE GOT TRESPASSERS.
SO I SEE.
TELL THEM TO GET THE FUCK OFF OUR LAND. TELL THEM THIS IS OUR TERRITORY. WE BOUGHT IT. WITHOUT SITTING TENANTS.
GO ON!
STUMPF TOOK SEVERAL SECONDS TO WORK OUT HIS PATTER, THEN SPOKE A FEW WILTING WORDS IN BAD PORTUGUESE.
NOS... ESTAMOS...ER... SOMOS DONOS DESTE TERRA...
THE PRONOUNCEMENT WAS MET WITH THE SAME BLANK LOOKS AS LOCKE'S PERFORMANCE.
STUMPF TRIED AGAIN, REARRANGING HIS INADEQUATE VOCABULARY TO TRY AND AWAKE A FLICKER OF UNDERSTANDING AMONGST THESE SAVAGES.
THE BOY STARED AT THE THIRD DEMON. HE WAS SICK AND HAGGARD; HE SMELT OF DEATH.

IF THEY DID UNDERSTAND, AND WERE FAKING BLANK INCOMPREHENSION, IT WAS A FLAWLESS PERFORMANCE.
THEY DON'T UNDERSTAND ME.
TELL THEM AGAIN.
I DON'T THINK THEY SPEAK PORTU-GUESE.
TELL THEM ANYWAY.

WE DON'T HAVE TO TALK TO THEM. THEY'RE ON OUR LAND. WE'RE WITHIN OUR RIGHTS--
NO. THERE'S NO NEED FOR SHOOTING. NOT IF WE CAN PERSUADE THEM TO GO PEACE-FULLY.
THEY DON'T UNDERSTAND PLAIN COMMON SENSE. LOOK AT THEM. THEY'RE ANIMALS, LIVING IN FILTH.

TELL THEM WE'VE GOT WORK TO DO HERE, THAT WE'VE GOT PAPERS.
I DON'T THINK THEY'D BE MUCH IMPRESSED.
JUST TELL THEM TO MOVE ON. FIND SOME OTHER PIECE OF LAND TO SQUAT ON.

WATCHING STUMPF PUT THESE SENTIMENTS INTO WORD AND SIGN LANGUAGE, LOCKE WAS ALREADY RUNNING THROUGH THE ALTERNATIVE OPTIONS AVAIL-ABLE. EITHER THE INDIANS ACCEPTED THEIR DEMANDS AND MOVED ON, OR ELSE THEY WOULD HAVE TO ENFORCE THE EDICT.

AS CHERRICK HAD SAID, THEY WERE WITHIN THEIR RIGHTS.

LOCKE HAD NO ACTIVE DESIRE TO SHED BLOOD. THE WORLD WAS TOO FULL OF BLEEDING HEART LIBERALS AND DOE-EYED SENTIMENTALISTS TO MAKE GENOCIDE THE MOST CONVE-NIENT SOLUTION.

BUT THE GUN HAD BEEN USED BEFORE, AND WOULD BE USED AGAIN, UNTIL EVERY UNWASHED INDIAN HAD PUT ON A PAIR OF TROUSERS AND GIVEN UP EATING MONKEYS.

INDEED, THE DIN OF LIBERALS NOTWITHSTANDING, THE GUN HAD ITS APPEAL. IT WAS SWIFT AND ABSOLUTE.

AT THE THOUGHT OF THESE SCARLET-FACED SAVAGES LAID LOW, LOCKE FELT HIS TRIGGER FINGER ITCH. PHYSICALLY *ITCH*.
STUMPF HAD FINISHED HIS ENCORE; IT HAD MET WITH NO RESPONSE.
I'M GOING TO BE SICK.
BE MY GUEST.
PLEASE. I HAVE TO LIE DOWN. I DON'T WANT THEM WATCHING ME.
YOU DON'T MOVE 'TIL THEY LISTEN. IF WE DON'T GET ANY JOY FROM THEM SOON, YOU'RE GOING TO SEE SOMETHING TO BE SICK ABOUT.
LOCKE TOYED WITH THE STOCK OF HIS RIFLE AS HE SPOKE, RUNNING A BROKEN THUMB-NAIL ALONG THE NICKS IN IT. THERE WERE PERHAPS A DOZEN. EACH ONE A HUMAN GRAVE.
THE JUNGLE CONCEALED MURDER SO EASILY; IT ALMOST SEEMED, IN ITS CRYPTIC FASHION, TO CONDONE THE CRIME.
FOR THE FIRST TIME SINCE THEIR APPEARANCE, ONE OF THE ASSEMBLY MOVED.
HE WAS AN ANCIENT; FULLY THIRTY YEARS OLDER THAN MOST OF THE TRIBE.
AND HE SPOKE...

WHAT EMERGED FROM HIS SCRAGGY THROAT WAS NOT A LANGUAGE MADE OF WORDS, BUT ONLY OF SOUND, A POTPOURRI OF JUNGLE NOISES. THERE WAS NO DISCERNIBLE PATTERN TO THE OUTPOURING; IT WAS SIMPLY A DISPLAY--AWESOME IN ITS WAY--OF IMPERSONATIONS.
THE MAN COULD MURMUR LIKE A JAGUAR, SCREECH LIKE A PARROT; HE COULD FIND IN HIS THROAT THE SLASH OF RAIN ON ORCHIDS, THE HOWL OF MONKEYS.
THE SOUNDS MADE STUMPF'S GORGE RISE.
THE JUNGLE HAD DISEASED HIM, DEHYDRATED HIM AND LEFT HIM WRUNG OUT. NOW THIS RHEUMY-EYED STICK-MAN WAS VOMITING THE WHOLE ODIOUS PLACE UP AT HIM.
WHAT'S HE SAYING?
WHAT DOES IT SOUND LIKE? IT'S ALL NOISES.
THE FUCKER'S CURSING US!
THE OLD MAN'S SONG-SPEECH LOWERED IN PITCH. HE WAS SINGING TWILIGHT, THAT BRIEF AMBIGUITY BETWEEN THE FIERCE DAY AND THE SUFFOCATING NIGHT.
WHAT ARE YOU SAYING? TALK SENSE!
BUT THE NIGHT-NOISES ONLY WHISPERED ON, AN UNBROKEN STREAM.
THIS IS OUR VILLAGE.

OUR VILLAGE. OUR LAND.
YOU SPEAK ENGLISH.
SOME.
WHY DIDN'T YOU ANSWER ME EARLIER?
NOT MY PLACE TO SPEAK. HE IS THE ELDER.
THE CHIEF, YOU MEAN?
THE CHIEF IS DEAD. ALL HIS FAMILY IS DEAD. THIS IS THE WISEST OF US--
THEN YOU TELL HIM--
NO NEED TO TELL. HE UNDERSTANDS YOU.
HE SPEAKS ENGLISH TOO?
NO. YOU ARE... TRANSPARENT.
TELL HIM ANYWAY, TELL THEM ALL. THIS IS OUR LAND. WE BOUGHT IT.
THE TRIBE HAS ALWAYS LIVED HERE.
NOT ANY LONGER.
WE'VE GOT PAPERS... FROM THE GOVERN-MENT.
WE WERE HERE BEFORE THE GOVERNMENT.

THEN, LIKE THE CLOSING OF A DEPARTING DAY, THE OLD MAN STOPPED TALKING THE FOREST.
HEY!
CALL HIM BACK! MAKE HIM TELL THE REST THEY'VE GOT TO GO.

AROUND THE COMPOUND, OTHERS WERE ALSO TURNING AWAY. THE OLD MAN'S WITHDRAWAL APPARENTLY SIGNALLED THAT THE SHOW WAS OVER.

NO!
YOU'RE NOT LISTENING!
DESPITE HIS HYSTERIA, HE WAS RAPIDLY LOSING HIS AUDIENCE.
YOU FUCKING SCUM!!
IT ONLY ENRAGED CHERRICK FURTHER.
LISTEN TO ME! LISTEN, YOU BASTARDS!
EASY...
CRAW
FROM WITHIN THE HUT CAME A TINY SHRIEK, NOT LIKE THE OLD MAN'S VOICE AT ALL.

AS THE SHRIEK SOUNDED, STUMPF FELL TO HIS KNEES, HIS GUT IN SPASM. HE DID NOT SEE THE DIMINUTIVE FIGURE EMERGE FROM THE HUT AND TOTTER INTO THE SUNLIGHT.

WHEN HE DID LOOK UP, AND SAW HOW THE CHILD WITH THE SCARLET FACE CLUTCHED HIS BELLY, STUMPF HOPED HIS EYES LIED.

BUT THEY DID NOT LIE.

SOMEWHERE AMONGST THE HUTS A WOMAN BEGAN TO SOB QUIETLY. FOR A MOMENT THE WORLD SPUN ON A PIN-HEAD, BALANCED EXQUISITELY BETWEEN SILENCE AND THE CRY THAT MUST BREAK IT, BETWEEN A TRUCE HELD AND THE COMING ATROCITY.

YOU STUPID BASTARD! BACK OFF! GET UP, STUMPF. WE'RE NOT WAITING.

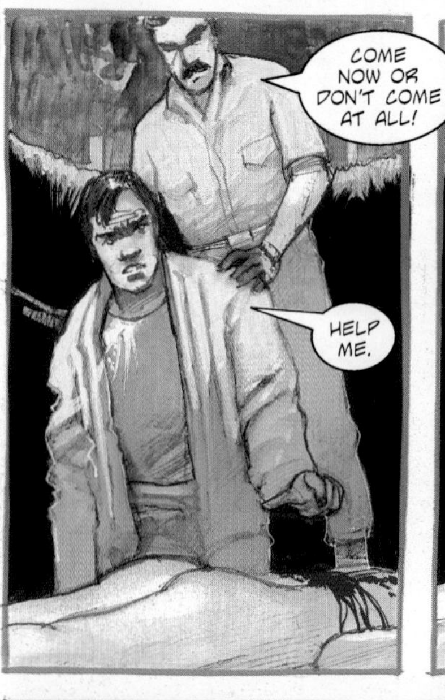

COME NOW OR DON'T COME AT ALL!
HELP ME.

COVER US, CHERRICK!

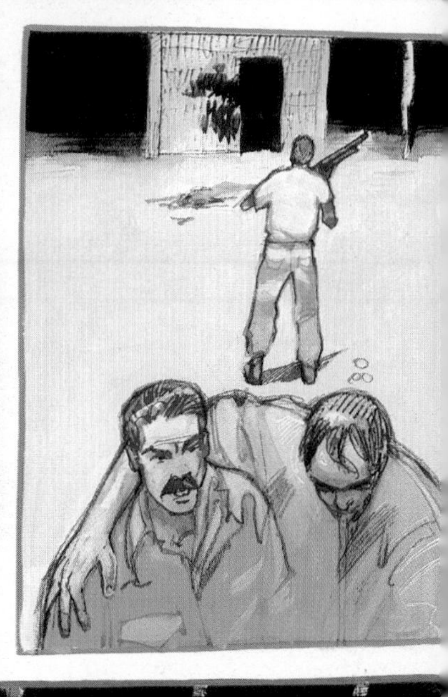

LOCKE AND STUMPF WERE ALREADY WITHIN TWENTY FEET OF THE JEEP, AND THERE WAS STILL NO MOVE FROM THE SAVAGES.

THEN, AS HE LOOKED BACK TOWARDS THE COMPOUND, IT SEEMED AS THOUGH THE TRIBE BREATHED TOGETHER ONE SOLID BREATH...

...AND HEARING THAT SOUND, CHERRICK FELT DEATH WEDGE ITSELF LIKE A FISH-BONE IN HIS THROAT, TOO DEEP TO BE PLUCKED OUT BY HIS FINGERS, TOO BIG TO BE SHAT.

IT WAS JUST WAITING THERE, LODGED IN CHERRICK'S ANATOMY, BEYOND ARGUMENT OR APPEAL.

HAD HE TOUCHED THE BOY? IF SO, IT HAD BEEN AN ASTONISHING SLEIGHT-OF-HAND, FOR CHERRICK HAD SEEN NOTHING.
TRICK OR NO TRICK, THE SIGNIFICANCE OF THE DISPLAY WAS PERFECTLY APPARENT: HE WAS BEING ACCUSED OF MURDER.
AS HE SPOKE HE SEEMED TO SEE A SHIFTING IN THE OLD MAN'S FEATURES.
YOU DON'T FRIGHTEN ME, YOU UNDERSTAND? I'M NOT A FOOL.
BENEATH THE CORRUPTION OF AGE, A HINT OF THE CHILD NOW DEAD AT THE HUT DOOR: THE TINY MOUTH EVEN SEEMED TO SMILE.
THEN, AS SUBTLY AS IT APPEARED, THE ILLUSION FADED.
AND CHERRICK WITHDREW.

THAT OLD BASTARD-- HUH?!

I TOUCHED HIM.

THE TINY TRADING POST TO THE SOUTH OF AVERIO WAS SCANT OF CIVILISATION, BUT IT SUFFICED. THERE WERE WHITE FACES HERE, AND CLEAN WATER. STUMPF, WHOSE CONDITION HAD DETERIORATED ON THE RETURN JOURNEY, WAS TREATED BY DANCY, AN ENGLISHMAN WHO HAD THE MANNER OF A DISENFRANCHISED EARL AND A FACE LIKE A HAMMERED STEAK.
IT WAS TETELMAN, THE OWNER OF THE TRADING POST'S STORES, WHO HAD THE MOST TO SAY WHEN THE REPORT WAS FINISHED.
BEBA GUARANA STOL
I'VE BEEN HERE YEARS. I KNOW THE WAY THESE PEOPLE THINK. THEY MAY ACT AS THOUGH THEY'RE STUPID-- COWARDS EVEN. TAKE IT FROM ME, THEY'RE NEITHER.

THEY DIDN'T MOVE ON US EVEN THOUGH THEY OUTNUMBERED US TEN TO ONE. IF THAT ISN'T COWARDICE, WHAT IS IT?
THIRTY YEARS AGO THIS WHOLE TERRITORY WAS THEIR HOMELAND. NOBODY WANTED IT. THEY WENT WHERE THEY LIKED, *DID* WHAT THEY LIKED. AS FAR AS THE WHITES WERE CONCERNED, THE JUNGLE WAS FILTHY AND DISEASE-INFECTED. WE WANTED NO PART OF IT.
AND, OF COURSE, IN SOME WAYS WE WERE RIGHT. IT *IS* FILTHY AND DISEASE-INFECTED; BUT IT'S ALSO GOT RESERVES WE NOW WANT BADLY: MINERALS, OIL MAYBE...POWER.
WE PAID FOR THE LAND. IT'S ALL WE'VE GOT NOW.
PAID?
THE MONKEY CHATTERED, APPARENTLY AS AMUSED BY THIS CLAIM AS ITS MASTER.
NO. YOU JUST PAID FOR A BLIND EYE, SO YOU COULD TAKE IT BY FORCE. YOU PAID FOR THE RIGHT TO FUCK UP THE INDIANS IN ANY WAY YOU COULD. THAT'S WHAT YOUR DOLLARS BOUGHT, MISTER LOCKE. THE GOVERNMENT OF THIS COUNTRY IS COUNTING OFF THE MONTHS UNTIL EVERY TRIBE ON THE SUB-CONTINENT IS WIPED OUT BY YOU OR YOUR LIKE.
SO WHY'D YOU COME HERE, IF YOU'RE SO FUCKING CLEVER?
SAME REASON AS YOU.
WHAT REASON IS THAT?
GREED.
I THOUGHT I COULD MAKE MY FORTUNE OUT HERE, THE SAME WAY YOU DO...I GAVE MYSELF TWO YEARS. THREE AT THE MOST. THAT WAS THE BEST PART OF TWO DECADES AGO.
THE JUNGLE EATS YOU UP AND SPITS YOU OUT, SOONER OR LATER.
NOT ME.
EXTINCTION'S IN THE AIR, MISTER LOCKE. I CAN SMELL IT.
THEY WON'T COME HERE, WILL THEY? THEY WON'T FOLLOW US?
THE QUESTION, SPOKEN IN ONLY A WHISPER, BEGGED FOR A REPLY IN THE NEGATIVE.
TRY AS HE MIGHT, CHERRICK COULD NOT DISLODGE THE SIGHTS OF THE PREVIOUS DAY.

DON'T FRET. SOMETIMES ONE OR TWO OF THEM WILL DRIFT IN HERE WITH A PARROT TO SELL, OR A FEW POTS, BUT I'VE NEVER SEEN THEM COME HERE IN ANY NUMBERS. THEY DON'T LIKE IT. THIS IS CIVILISATION AS FAR AS THEY'RE CONCERNED, AND IT INTIMIDATES THEM. BESIDES, THEY WOULDN'T HARM MY GUESTS. THEY NEED ME.
NEED YOU?
THEY USE OUR MEDICINES. DANCY SUPPLIES THEM. AND BLANKETS, ONCE IN A WHILE. AS I SAID, THEY'RE NOT STUPID.

YAAAHAARRG!
YOUR FRIEND'S GONE BAD.
NO FRIEND.
NEXT DOOR STUMPF HAD BEGUN TO HOWL. DANCY'S CONSOLING VOICE COULD BE HEARD, ATTEMPTING TO TALK DOWN THE PANIC. HE WAS PLAINLY FAILING.

IT ROTS.
WHAT DOES?
THE SOUL. IT'S LIKE FRUIT, YOU SEE. IT ROTS.
STUMPF'S CRIES GAVE FORCE TO THE OBSERVATION. IT WAS NOT THE VOICE OF A WHOLESOME CREATURE; THERE WAS PUTRESCENCE IN IT.

WHAT DO THEY GIVE YOU FOR THE MEDICINES AND BLANKETS? WOMEN?
I'VE NO USE FOR WOMEN. I'VE HAD THE SYPH FOR TOO MANY YEARS. THE SOUL...ISN'T THE ONLY THING THAT ROTS.
WELL, WHAT DO YOU GET FROM THEM THEN? FOR YOUR SUPPLIES?
ARTIFACTS. BOWLS, JUGS, MATS. EVERYBODY WANTS SOMETHING MADE BY AN EXTINCT TRIBE THESE DAYS. *MEMENTO MORI.*
EXTINCT?
THE WORD HAD A SEDUCTIVE RING; IT SOUNDED LIKE LIFE TO HIM.
OH, CERTAINLY, THEY'RE AS GOOD AS GONE. IF YOU DON'T WIPE THEM OUT, THEY'LL DO IT THEMSELVES.
SUICIDE?
IN THEIR FASHION. A TRIBE LOSES ITS LAND, AND ITS APPETITE FOR LIFE GOES WITH IT. THE WOMEN DON'T GET PREGNANT ANYMORE; THE YOUNG MEN TAKE TO DRINK, THE OLD MEN JUST STARVE THEMSELVES TO DEATH. IN A YEAR OR TWO IT'S LIKE THEY NEVER EXISTED.
LOCKE SILENTLY SALUTED THE FATAL WISDOM OF THESE PEOPLE. THEY KNEW WHEN TO DIE, WHICH WAS MORE THAN COULD BE SAID FOR SOME HE'D MET. THE THOUGHT OF THEIR DEATH-WISH ABSOLVED HIM OF ANY LAST VESTIGES OF GUILT.
WHAT WAS THE GUN IN HIS HAND, EXCEPT AN INSTRUMENT OF EVOLUTION?

ON THE FOURTH DAY OF THEIR ARRIVAL AT THE POST, STUMPF'S FEVER ABATED, MUCH TO DANCY'S DISAPPOINTMENT.
THE WORST OF IT'S OVER. GIVE HIM TWO MORE DAYS REST AND YOU CAN HEAD BACK TO YOUR LABORS.
TIME TO GET OURSELVES SOME HELP AND GO BACK IN THERE.
BUT NO MORE GUNS.
CHERRICK HADN'T TOUCHED HIS RIFLE SINCE THEY'D ARRIVED AT THE POST: IN FACT, HE KEPT FROM CONTACT WITH ANYTHING BUT A BOTTLE AND HIS BED.
HIS SKIN SEEMED TO CRAWL AND CREEP PERPETUALLY.
NO NEED FOR GUNS.
IF YOU MEAN WAITING FOR THEM TO DIE OUT NATURALLY, I'M NOT THAT PATIENT.
NO, WE CAN BE SWIFTER THAN THAT.
HOW?
THEY'RE MY LIVELIHOOD, OR PART OF IT. YOU'RE ASKING ME TO HELP YOU MAKE MYSELF BANKRUPT.
WHAT'S IT WORTH? YOUR WISDOM?
A CUT OF WHATEVER YOU FIND ON YOUR LAND.
ALL RIGHT, TETELMAN, TALK.
THEY NEED MEDICINES BECAUSE THEY'RE SO SUSCEPTIBLE TO OUR DISEASES. A DECENT PLAGUE CAN WIPE THEM OUT PRACTICALLY OVERNIGHT.
ONE FELL SWOOP. THEY'VE GOT PRACTICALLY NO DEFENCES AGAINST CERTAIN BACTERIA. NEVER HAD TO BUILD UP ANY RESISTANCE. THE CLAP. SMALLPOX. EVEN MEASLES.
HOW?
I ASKED HOW?
BLANKETS.
DEAD MEN'S BLANKETS.

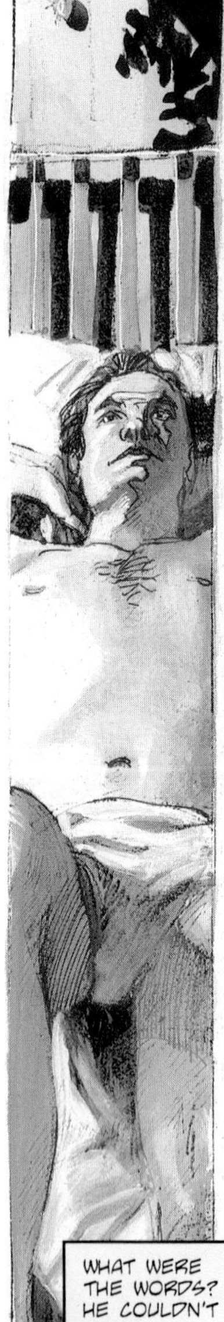
A LITTLE BEFORE DAWN OF THE NIGHT OF STUMPF'S RECOVERY, CHERRICK WOKE SUDDENLY, STARTLED FROM HIS REST BY BAD DREAMS.
IT WAS THE WORDS HE DREAMT. WORDS COMING FROM THE OLD MAN'S TOOTHLESS MOUTH WHICH BROUGHT ON THE COLD SWEATS THAT ENCASED HIS BODY.
WHAT WERE THE WORDS? HE COULDN'T RECALL THEM NOW.

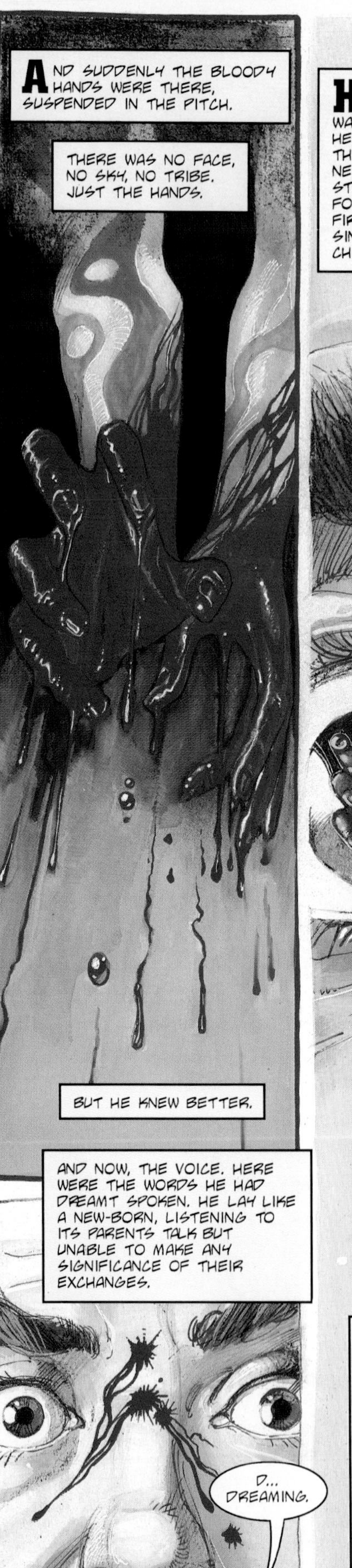
AND SUDDENLY THE BLOODY HANDS WERE THERE, SUSPENDED IN THE PITCH.
THERE WAS NO FACE, NO SKY, NO TRIBE. JUST THE HANDS.
BUT HE KNEW BETTER.
AND NOW, THE VOICE. HERE WERE THE WORDS HE HAD DREAMT SPOKEN. HE LAY LIKE A NEW-BORN, LISTENING TO ITS PARENTS TALK BUT UNABLE TO MAKE ANY SIGNIFICANCE OF THEIR EXCHANGES.
D... DREAMING.

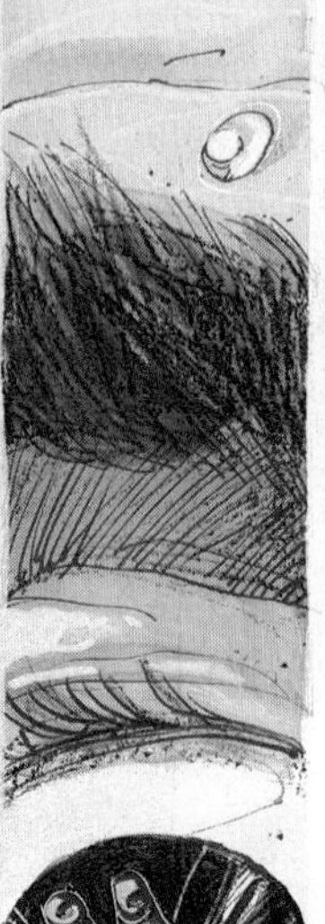
HE WAS IGNORANT, WASN'T HE? HE TASTED THE SOURNESS OF HIS STUPIDITY FOR THE FIRST TIME SINCE CHILDHOOD.
THE VOICE MADE HIM FEARFUL OF AMBIGUITIES HE HAD RIDDEN ROUGHSHOD OVER, OF WHISPERS HIS SHOUTING LIFE HAD RENDERED INAUDIBLE.
HE STRUGGLED, WISHING HE COULD STOP THE VOICE AND ASK FOR EXPLANATION.
BUT IT WAS ALREADY FADING.
HE FUMBLED FOR COMPREHENSION, AND WAS NOT ENTIRELY FRUSTRATED. THE MAN WAS SPEAKING OF THE WORLD, AND OF EXILE FROM THE WORLD, OF BEING BROKEN ALWAYS BY WHAT ONE SEEKS TO POSSESS.

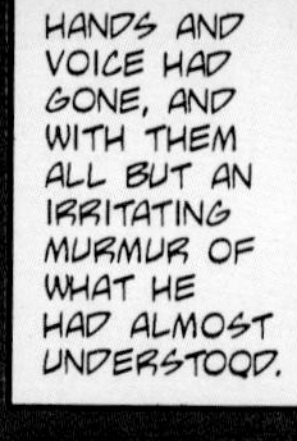
HANDS AND VOICE HAD GONE, AND WITH THEM ALL BUT AN IRRITATING MURMUR OF WHAT HE HAD ALMOST UNDERSTOOD.

HIS BACK AND BUTTOCKS, AND THE UNDERSIDE OF HIS THIGHS, FELT SORE.
THERE WAS AGAIN THE ITCH OF TENDERNESS IN HIS SKIN THAT HE'D SUFFERED SINCE COMING TO THE POST. HE WANTED TO BE AWAY FROM THIS PLACE, AND BADLY.
THERE WAS A CUT IN THE CUSHION OF HIS THUMB, WHERE THE MOSQUITO NET HAD NICKED HIS FLESH.
THE CLOTHES HE PUT ON WERE A SCOURGE TO HIS BACK. HE SEEMED TO FEEL EVERY THREAD CHAFING HIS NERVE ENDINGS.
HE FELT STRANGE. THERE WAS SOMETHING ABOUT THIS DAWNING DAY WHICH MADE HIM PROFOUNDLY UNEASY. HE KNEW THE DANGERS OF COURTING UNFOUNDED FEARS, AND HE TRIED TO FORBID THEM, BUT THEY WERE INCONTESTABLE.
ZZZZZ
NEVERMORE
TAP
ZZZZZ
IT WASN'T THE BLOOD OF THE INSECT, BUT HIS OWN.

STUMPF'S NOT FIT FOR THIS KIND OF WORK. AND CHERRICK--
WHAT ABOUT ME?
YOU'RE PARANOID. PARANOID AND UNRE-LIABLE.
JUST BECAUSE I KILLED SOME INDIAN BRAT!
YOU JUST DIDN'T HAVE THE BALLS TO DO IT YOURSELF!
ARE YOU LISTENING TO ME?
AAAGH!
TUMP!
THROUGH THE DIN OF PAIN IN HIS HEAD HE COULD HEAR A QUIET VOICE. THE WORDS WERE INAUDIBLE, BUT HE KNEW WHOSE THEY WERE.
I WON'T HEAR!
I WON'T HEAR, DAMN YOU!

WHAT THE HELL'S HE TALKING ABOUT?
HE SPOKE TO ME. THE OLD MAN.
YOU MEAN AT THE VILLAGE. IS THAT WHAT YOU MEAN?
HE WANTS US OUT. EXILES. LIKE THEM. *LIKE THEM!*
I BELIEVE YOU. JUST SLOW DOWN. WE CAN SORT IT OUT.
NO. IT'S PUSHING US OUT. EVERYTHING WE TOUCH. EVERYTHING WE TOUCH...
WHAT'S HAPPENING TO ME?
LET ME HELP.
NO DON'T TOUCH ME!
IT'S ALL RIGHT.
IT WASN'T. DANCY FELT THE FLESH SLIP AWAY FROM THE BONE. THE SENSATION BESTED EVEN HIS TASTE FOR AGONY.
HE'S ROTTING...
THERE WAS NO HELP FOR HIM. ALL THE OTHERS COULD DO WAS STAND AROUND LIKE SPECTATORS AT AN EXECUTION, AWAITING THE FINAL THROES.

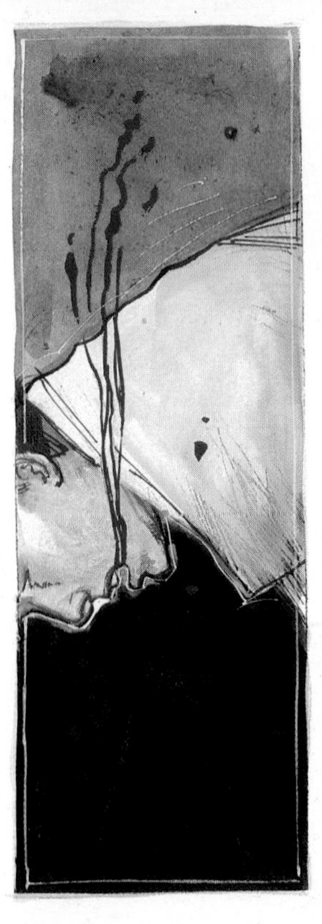

IS HE DEAD?
ALMOST.
ROTTED.

WHAT ARE YOU SAYING?

YOU WANT TO GIVE ME YOUR SHARE OF THE LAND?
THERE'S WITNESSES HERE. JUST SAY YES. THEY'LL HEAR YOU. JUST SAY YES.
DANCY, YOU HEAR WHAT HE SAID?

DEEP IN HIS BODY, CHERRICK FELT THE FISH-BONE HE'D FIRST CHOKED ON IN THE VILLAGE TWIST ITSELF ABOUT ONE FINAL TIME, AND EXTINGUISH HIM.
DANCY, YOU'RE A WITNESS.
IF YOU MUST.

DID HE SAY YES, DANCY?
HE SAID YES.

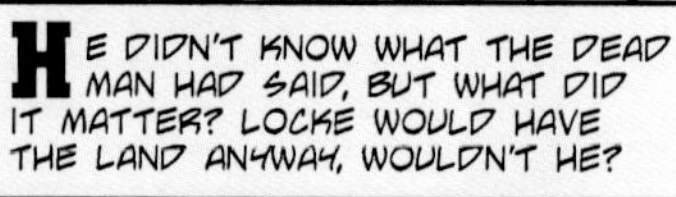
HE DIDN'T KNOW WHAT THE DEAD MAN HAD SAID, BUT WHAT DID IT MATTER? LOCKE WOULD HAVE THE LAND ANYWAY, WOULDN'T HE?

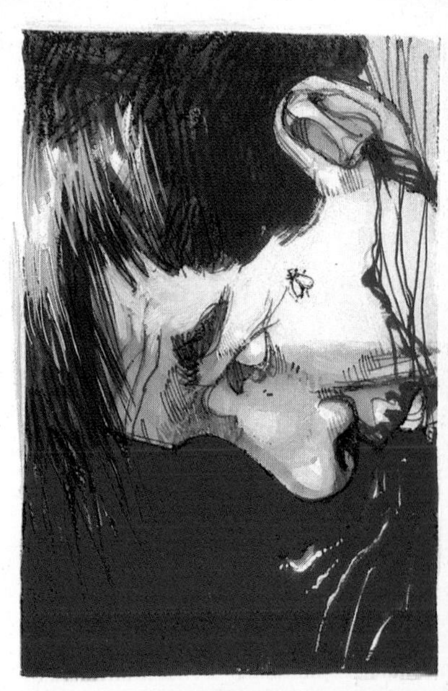

THEY HAD BURIED HIM TOWARDS EVENING. THE CORPSE HAD BEGUN TO PUTREFY BY THE TIME IT WAS SEWN UP IN CANVAS FOR THE BURIAL.
THE NIGHT FOLLOWING, STUMPF HAD COME TO LOCKE AND OFFERED HIM THE LAST THIRD OF THE TERRITORY TO ADD TO CHERRICK'S SHARE.
LOCKE, EVER THE REALIST, HAD ACCEPTED.
THE EVENING OF THE NEXT DAY, AS STUMPF HAD HOPED, THE SUPPLY PLANE CAME IN.
LK1015
LOCKE ELECTED TO FLY BACK TO SANTAREM TO BUY UP FRESH SUPPLIES AND, IF POSSIBLE, HIRE A RELIABLE DRIVER AND GUNMAN.
AT SANTAREM, THEY PARTED WITH A SINGLE HANDSHAKE WHICH LEFT EVERY NERVE IN STUMPF'S HAND SCOURGED...
...AN OPEN CUT IN THE TENDER FLESH BETWEN HIS INDEX FINGER AND THUMB.

SANTAREM WASN'T RIO, LOCKE MUSED, AS HE MADE HIS WAY DOWN TO A BAR AT THE SOUTH END OF TOWN, IN SEARCH OF THE KIND OF LOCAL ENTERTAINMENT OF WHICH HE NEVER TIRED.

THE WOMEN OF SANTAREM WERE AS UNPALATABLE AS THE BEER, BUT LOCKE HAD NO EYE FOR BEAUTY IN THE OPPOSITE SEX: HIS PLEASURE WAS IN SEEING JUST WHAT A WOMAN WOULD DO FOR A FEW GRUBBY DOLLAR BILLS.

HE HAD FINALLY FOUND ONE WHO--ONCE DRUNKENNESS HAD PERSUADED HER TO ABANDON WHAT LITTLE HOPE OF DIGINITY SHE HAD--WAS WILLING TO ACCEDE TO A PARTICULAR PECCADILLO...

MENSAGEM, SENHOR LOCKE. HOSPITAL SACRADO CORAGÃO DE MARIA.
IT COULD ONLY BE STUMPF, LOCKE THOUGHT. WHO ELSE DID HE KNOW IN THIS CORNER OF HELL WHO'D CALL UPON HIM?
VEM COMIGO. VEM COMIGO. URGENTE.

NO, I'M NOT COMING. NOT NOW. YOU UNDERSTAND? LATER. LATER.
TA MORRENDO.
DYING? WELL, LET HIM. UNDERSTAND ME? YOU GO BACK AND TELL HIM I WON'T COME UNTIL I'M READY.

E MEU DINHEIRO?
YOU GO TO HELL.
WHEN, TWO HOURS AND ONE UNGAINLY ACT OF PASSIONLESS SEX LATER, LOCKE UNLOCKED THE DOOR, HE DISCOVERED THAT THE CHILD, BY WAY OF REVENGE, HAD DEFECATED ON THE THRESHOLD.

THE HOSPITAL SACRADO CORAGÃO DE MARIA WAS NO PLACE TO FALL ILL; BETTER, THOUGHT LOCKE, TO DIE IN YOUR OWN BED WITH YOUR OWN SWEAT FOR COMPANY.
HERE. YOUR FRIEND. HE'S HURT HIS EYE, AND HE HAS SOME MINOR ABRASIONS ON HIS HANDS AND FACE, BUT HE WON'T HAVE ANYONE GO NEAR HIM.
JUST PAYS FOR THE CLEAN ROOM AND DOCTORS HIMSELF.
HE HAS DELUSIONS. TELL HIM HE PAY MORE OR TOMORROW HE LEAVES.

LOCKE WAS LOOKING AT THE MAN FOR A GOOD TIME BEFORE STUMPF SENSED THAT HE WAS WATCHED. HE LOOKED UP SLOWLY.
HIS GOOD EYE, AS IF IN COMPENSATION FOR THE LOSS OF ITS COMPANION, SEEMED TO HAVE SWELLED TO TWICE ITS NATURAL SIZE. IT HELD ENOUGH FEAR FOR BOTH IT AND ITS TWIN; INDEED ENOUGH FOR A DOZEN EYES.

EVERYTHING IS TRUE, LOCKE. EVERYTHING.
WHAT THE HELL ARE YOU TALKING ABOUT?
TETELMAN TOLD ME--CHERRICK'S BABBLING, ABOUT BEING EXILES...*THE ELDER*. FROM THE VILLAGE. *HE WAS HERE*, STANDING WHERE YOU'RE STANDING, LOOKING AT ME THROUGH THE GLASS.

IT HAPPENED TO CHERRICK, AND NOW IT'S HAPPENING TO ME. NONE OF US'LL ESCAPE. NOT UNLESS WE MAKE AMENDS.
LOOK, YOU'VE GOT TO VACATE THE ROOM. I'VE BEEN TOLD YOU'VE GOT TO GET OUT BY MORNING.
NO, I CAN'T LEAVE. I *CAN'T LEAVE.*
THE DUST. THE DUST IN THE AIR. IT'LL CUT ME UP. I GOT A SPECK IN MY EYE--JUST A *SPECK*--AND THE NEXT THING MY EYE'S BLEEDING AS THOUGH IT'LL NEVER STOP. I CAN'T HARDLY LIE DOWN. THE SHEET'S LIKE A BED OF NAILS. YOU'VE GOT TO HELP ME.
HOW?
PAY THEM FOR THE ROOM. PAY THEM SO I CAN STAY 'TIL YOU GET A SPECIALIST FROM SAO LUIS. THEN GO BACK TO THE VILLAGE, LOCKE. GO BACK AND TELL THEM. I DON'T WANT THE LAND. TELL THEM I DON'T OWN IT ANY LONGER.
I'LL GO BACK, BUT IN MY OWN GOOD TIME.
TELL THEM TO LET ME BE. PLEASE.
THERE'S NOTHING THERE.
HE'S HERE.
MY GOD.
WHAT'S HAPPENING?
SEE?
WHAT ARE YOU PLAYING AT? YOU HAVEN'T GOT CHERRICK'S DISEASE. YOU CAN'T HAVE. YOU DIDN'T TOUCH THEM. WE *AGREED*, DAMN YOU. CHERRICK TOUCHED THEM--*WE DIDNT*.
WE WERE WRONG.
THIS ISN'T SOMETHING YOU CAN BEAT INTO SUBMISSION, LOCKE. IT'S OUT OF OUR HANDS.
SEE?

STUMPF'S SUDDEN, FATALISTIC CALM FRIGHTENED LOCKE.
THE ROOM WAS LOCKED. THE KEY WAS ON THE INSIDE, WHERE STUMPF HAD PAID FOR IT TO BE.
KEEP OUT. KEEP AWAY FROM ME.
KEEP OUT, I SAID! NO!
SOMEHWERE NEARBY A WOMAN BEGAN TO YELL. NO MATTER; LOCKE WOULD HAVE HIS HANDS ON THE GERMAN BEFORE HELP COULD COME...
...AND THEN, BY CHRIST, HE'D WIPE EVERY LAST VESTIGE OF A SMILE FROM THE BASTARD'S LIPS.
IN THE ANTISEPTIC COCOON OF HIS ROOM, STUMPF FELT THE FIRST BLAST OF UNCLEAN AIR FROM THE OUTSIDE WORLD. IT WAS NO MORE THEN A LIGHT BREEZE THAT INVADED HIS MAKESHIFT SANCTUARY, BUT IT BORE UPON ITS BACK THE DEBRIS OF THE WORLD.
SOOT AND SEEDS, FLAKES OF SKIN ITCHED OFF A THOUSAND SCALPS, FLUFF AND SAND AND TWIST OF HAIR, THE BRIGHT DUST FROM A MOTH'S WING.
AAIIIEEEE!
MOTES SO SMALL THE HUMAN EYE ONLY GLIMPSED THEM IN A SHAFT OF WHITE SUNLIGHT, EACH A TINY, WHIRLING SPECK QUITE HARMLESS TO MOST LIVING ORGANISMS.
BUT THIS CLOUD WAS LETHAL TO STUMPF; IN SECONDS HIS BODY BECAME A FIELD OF TINY, SEEPING WOUNDS.

AAAGH!
LOCKE, REALIZING THAT STUMPF WAS PAST RECANTING HIS LAUGHTER, LET THE MAN GO.
THE KILLING AIR STILL SLICED HIM AS HE SANK DOWN; WITH EACH AGONIZED SHUDDER HE WOKE IN THE AIR NEW EDDIES AND WHIRLPOOLS TO OPEN HIM UP.

SANGUE
COLABORE

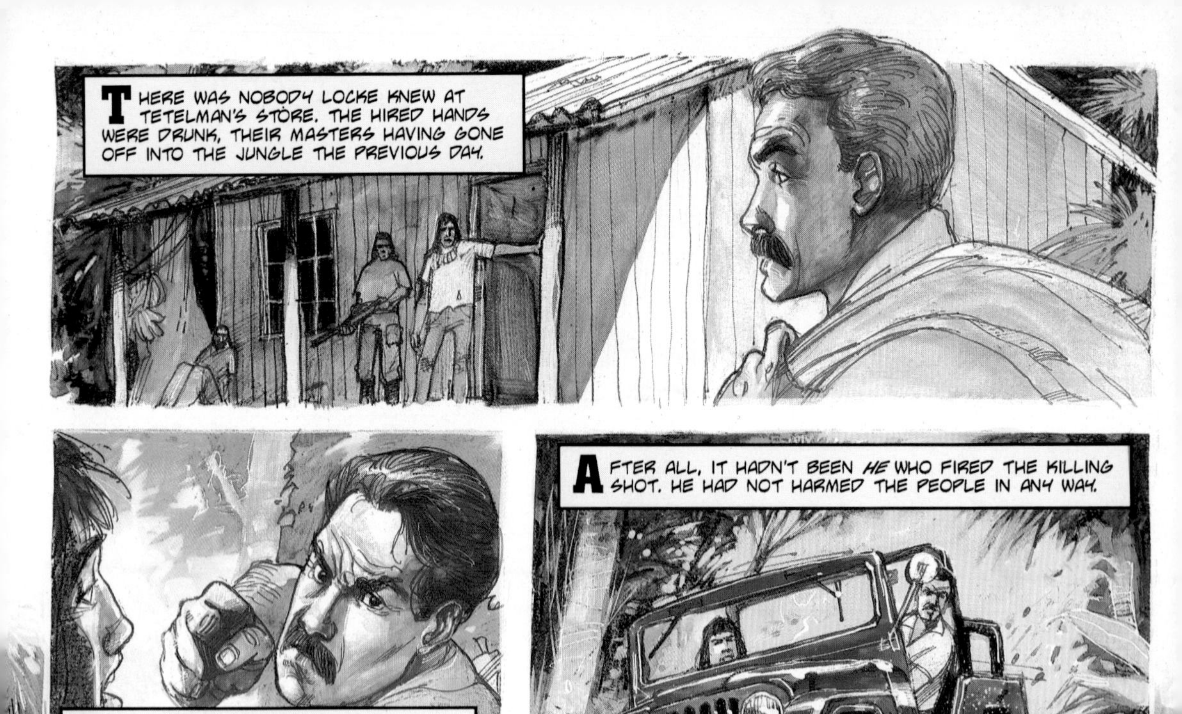
THERE WAS NOBODY LOCKE KNEW AT TETELMAN'S STORE. THE HIRED HANDS WERE DRUNK, THEIR MASTERS HAVING GONE OFF INTO THE JUNGLE THE PREVIOUS DAY.
LOCKE PERSUADED THE MOST SOBER OF THE MEN TO ACCOMPANY HIM BACK TO THE VILLAGE AS TRANSLATOR.
HE HAD NO REAL IDEA OF HOW HE WOULD MAKE HIS PEACE WITH THE TRIBE. HE WAS ONLY CERTAIN THAT HE HAD TO ARGUE HIS INNOCENCE.
AFTER ALL, IT HADN'T BEEN HE WHO FIRED THE KILLING SHOT. HE HAD NOT HARMED THE PEOPLE IN ANY WAY.
IF THEY SHOULD REQUIRE SOME PENANCE OF HIM, HE WAS NOT ABOVE ACCEDING TO THEIR DEMANDS. HE HAD SEEN SO MUCH SUFFERING OF LATE. HE WANTED TO BE CLEANSED OF IT.

ANYTHING THEY ASKED, WITHIN REASON, HE WOULD COMPLY WITH, ANYTHING TO AVOID DYING LIKE THE OTHERS. HE'D EVEN GIVE BACK THE LAND.
WHERE ARE YOU?
MY GOD, WHAT ARE YOU DOING HERE?
I MIGHT ASK YOU THE SAME QUESTION.
MISTER LOCKE. IT IS GOOD WE MEET.

AN EDUCATION.

THE MINGLED SMELLS OF LIME AND PETROL CANCELLED OUT ANY OTHER SCENT.

ALL OF THEM?
BLANKETS.
ONE FELL SWOOP.
BUT SO QUICKLY...
IT'S VERY EFFICIENT. AND DIFFICULT TO PROVE. EVEN IF ANYBODY EVER ASKS.
DISEASE IS NATURAL, YES? LIKE THE TREES.
I HEAR GOOD THINGS OF YOU. PERHAPS WE CAN WORK TOGETHER.
THE ELDER BORE A NEAT BULLET-HOLE IN HIS TEMPLE. DISEASE AND HOPELESSNESS HAD NOT BEEN ENTIRELY EFFICIENT, APPARENTLY.
WE THOUGHT YOU WOULDN'T COME BACK.
STUMPF IS DEAD.
SO IT GOES.
WELL, EVEN LESS TO DIVIDE UP.
FIN